Train your Brain

Written by Ryuta Kawashima
Translated by Ryoken Fujito

To Mampei, Kosuke, Mizuki, and Katsuya

●

First published in Japan, 2001, Kumon Publishing Co.,Ltd.

Designed by Kazuo Miyagawa
Illustrated by Kazuya Takada, Kazuharu Yoshitsugu

ISBN4－7743－0728－9

Kumon Publishing Co., Ltd.
Goban-cho Grand Bldg.3-1, Goban-cho,
Chiyoda-ku Tokyo Japan
Printed in Japan.
First edition, Dec.,2003/06-02-104

Contents

Contents

Chapter 6
Your mind is in your brain 70

Chapter 7
Conclusion: Train your brain by yourself 82

Welcome to the World of the Brain

If I asked you where your brain was what would you say? You'd say it's in your head, right? That was an easy one.

If I asked you what your brain was what would you say? Now that's not so easy to answer, is it? Maybe some of you are saying "Why are you starting out with such a bizarre question" or "If it's going to be like this, I don't know if I can finish reading this book." The fact is, though, at this very moment you are using your brain to answer these questions. That's the brain. What's that you say? This is already getting too complicated for you? Well, not only answering the questions, but finding, picking up, opening and reading this book are all activities directed by the brain. Even your answer that the brain is in the head came from your brain.

So, have I confused you even more? Well, I have a confession. That's my brain telling me to start this book by asking you confusing questions.

Let's look at the handiwork of the brain

We can perform many tasks because our brains are working. Although we can talk about the handiwork of the brain now, people began studying the brain only about 100 years ago. Even today there are still many things about the brain we do not understand.

My colleagues and I are working in the difficult field of brain science. Brain science tries to solve the mysteries of brain activity. Step-by-step we aim to someday be able to explain all of the brain's activities. The brain is so interesting to me that I never get tired of studying it. Although our goal is 100%, so far we have only about 10% of the whole story. At universities and other institutions around the world brain scientists are studying the brain to learn the rest of the story. I am engaged in brain imaging research, which looks into the functions of the brain by means of imaging. I am going to introduce the results of my study in this book.

I would like to start out by relating an experiment about something you might never get tired of: video games. Actually, my expectations

Chapter 1

Welcome to the World of the Brain

and the results of this experiment were completely different, but thanks to it my interest in the brain really began to take off.

When do we use the brain more: playing a video game or doing calculations?

Let me begin my story by giving you a little background about myself: After I graduated from college I entered graduate school to continue my studies. When I began studying the functions of the brain in graduate school, brain science was not very popular, and there was no money available for research. Then a device for detecting brain activity was invented. Using it we could examine how the brain worked during certain human activities. Since we can't cut open the head and take out the brain, this invention was a godsend for all brain scientists. With it we could see images of the brain. I couldn't wait to proceed with my studies using the device, but I soon found out that there was no money to buy one. I had never in my life been

more disappointed. My colleagues and I in the laboratory talked about this and that possibility to get money for our research. Then we thought "What is the most profitable company around?" This was when video games were rapidly becoming popular. That's it! Your brain must work very hard when you play a video game, seeing as how you use your eyes, ears, hands and mind so much.

I will explain the details later, but for now let me say that in the same way as the more you exercise, the stronger you become, the harder the brain works, the more powerful the brain becomes.

A plan was hatched in my brain. I would study how the brain worked while playing a video game, and when I got the results I expected, I would bring them to the video game company and tell them what I was sure they wanted to hear: While you are playing a video game your brain is working very hard and getting more and more powerful, therefore playing video games is the best way to train your brain! I was sure the company would jump at the chance to fund our research.

In the game I chose for the experiment you can control the character's movements, such as the arms, legs, jumping, etc. I am sure you know what sort of game I am talking about. I figured you would have to use the brain a lot to decide the direction the character should move, keep your eyes on the character on the display, operate the hand controls, and such. Then an idea came to me. In order to confirm my results, I should have an experiment under conditions that were the opposite of having fun. What is a dull and boring activity? I decided to use the "Uchida-Kraepelin Psycho Diagnostic Test" that I took several times when I was in highschool. In this test there are 116 single digits. You write the sum of two adjoining digits in the space between them. If the sum is over 10 then you write only the last single digit. You continue in this way on the first row for up to 60 seconds, and then go on to the next row. The test lasts 35 minutes, including a 5 minute break. Your speed and accuracy are said to indicate your character and aptitude for certain jobs. Try the sample test on page 15. The calculation itself is very easy, but it's hard to continue for 30 minutes. Even though I was very good at math, I hated this test. I couldn't stand wasting all that time.

I was sure that the brain would be much more active while playing a video game. Don't you agree? Let's look at the results. I used the latest model apparatus, the Positron CT, for the experiment. Look at Fig.2.

Fig.1

$$7\ _{6}9\ _{3}4\ _{0}6\ _{9}3\ _{/}8\ 6\ 7\ 5$$
$$3\ 8\ 5\ 9\ 8\ 7\ 6\ 5\ 4$$
$$8\ 7\ 4\ 9\ 8\ 4\ 7\ 3\ 8$$
$$4\ 7\ 8\ 6\ 5\ 3\ 9\ 5\ 8$$
$$8\ 3\ 5\ 9\ 4\ 8\ 7\ 5\ 3$$

"Uchida-Kraepelin Psychodiagnostic Test" (sample) and how to take.

Chapter 1

Welcome to the World of the Brain

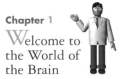

It looks like a box. I had the subjects, who were my students, lay

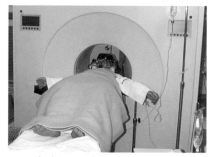

Fig.2: The latest model apparatus "Positron CT" for the experiment.

face up in the apparatus. Then I could see a picture of the brain at work while the subject was doing something. Fig.3 shows you the results with five college student subjects. The image of the brain was sliced from the bottom to the top upwards, and you can see the images in order from left to right in Fig.3. The top of the cross section is the forehead side, and the bottom is the back of the head. Of course we

Fig.3

While playing a video game.

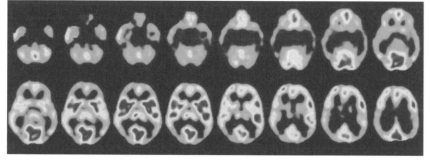

While taking the Kraepelin Test.

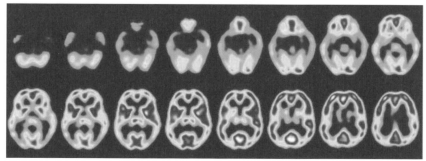

Fig.4

While playing a video game.

right

front

left · back

While taking the Kraepelin Test.

right

front

left · back

never actually sliced the brain! Thanks to the latest technology we could look at the human brain in this way. In order to understand it more easily I have added a three-dimensional view. Fig.4. Going from left to right, the first cross section is the forehead, the eye is second, and the ear is third. The green, yellow, red and white areas indicate the energy from food that is being used by the brain. The white and red areas indicate that a lot of energy is being consumed, which means the brain is working very hard. So, does the brain work harder while you are playing a

video game or calculating? You can tell at a glance. I was shocked at the results. Monotonous work like adding single digit figures makes the brain work harder than a fun activity like playing a video game. This was the complete opposite of my expectations! I had failed utterly. The long awaited results would never convince a video game company to fund our research. "Inconceivable. This should never have happened. The results must be wrong?" I thought. Regrettably, the same results were confirmed in another experiment using a different machine.

Chapter 1

Welcome to the World of the Brain

11

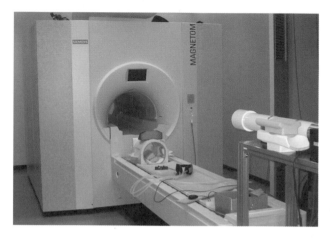

Fig.5
The apparatus "f MRI"
for the experiment.

Opening the door to the world of the brain

We have another device called fMRI (functional Magnetic Resonance Imaging). This can show us three-dimensional images of the brain by using color to indicate where the brain is actively working. Take a look at Fig.6. The figure shows a brain image of a 7th grade (12 years old) student doing single digit addition. The red area indicates the places where the brain is working hard. A college student and a seventh grader would show the same image of the brain when they are doing easy calculations.

Now then, you have read this book up to this point. Perhaps some of you are wondering: "What is so good about the brain being active in so many places?" My assumption that playing a video game must make the brain work hard turned out to be wrong. Instead, it was confirmed that the brain was more active when doing simple calculations like those on the Uchida-Kraepelin Test. This is the point that I would like to address in this book.

Now I would like to give you an analogy. If you use your legs a lot running every day, your leg muscles will develop. If you use your arms a lot doing push-ups every day, your arm muscles will develop. Once

When a seventh grade student is doing single digit addition.

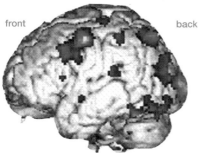
front · back

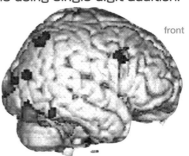
front

Fig.6 Left-hemisphere · Right-hemisphere

your muscles are strong, you can use your power and become better at any sport. The same is true for the brain. If you solve a lot of calculations, just like running every day, many places in your brain will become active and develop. Once your brain is strong, you can use it to manage all kinds of difficult tasks. Now you know the story. Brain activity helps the brain develop, and the result is a strong brain.

I invite you to take a tour of the latest frontiers in medicine, some of which I am personally involved with. Investigating the "latest frontiers" sounds very difficult, but in fact it isn't. It is research to find answers to the following questions:

How does the brain work when we read a book, listen to music, solve word problems and move the body?

Is there any method of study that will make the brain stronger or sharper?

Is it true that finger exercises help to develop the brain?

What activity of the brain causes likes and dislikes?

I will answer these questions and explain other riddles as well in this book.

Let's start. Enter the world of the brain through the door my colleagues and I have opened, and you will see all its mysteries and wonders.

Chapter 1

Welcome to the World of the Brain

Understanding more about the brain —1
The right and left brain

I wonder if any of you scratched your heads when you first laid eyes on the words right brain and left brain in this chapter. Well it's true: we have two brains, a right and a left, the same as two eyes, ears, hands, legs and so on. In our body we have two lungs and two kidneys. Why do we have two instead of one? This is a mystery about our brains and bodies that no one has solved yet. Unlike other organs such as the eyes and ears, only the brain seems to have different functions for each side. In right-handers, the left brain controls the function of understanding and speaking words. On the other hand the right brain seems to control nonverbal communication tasks such as understanding people's expressions and gestures. This is what our latest studies tell us. (See page 73 for details.)

The other side of the brain can compensate if one side of the brain has been damaged or is not working properly. In this way, although the two sides of the brain have their own jobs, they can cover for each other in a pinch.

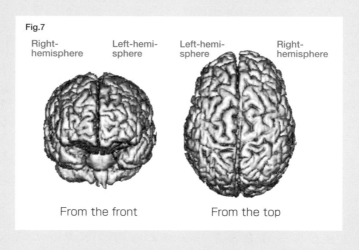

Fig.7

Right-hemisphere   Left-hemisphere   Left-hemisphere   Right-hemisphere

From the front   From the top

Let's try 1

You can practice my experiments by following these instructions. Even without using special equipment, your brain will work the same as explained on pages 10, 11, and 13.

●How to do it:

1. Refer to the example on page 9 and write the sum of two adjoining digits in the space between them. If the sum is over 10 write only the last single digit. On the actual test there are 116 digits in a line, but here you have only 24.

2. On the actual test you write the sum between the figures; here you can read the answers aloud.

3. On the actual test you move to the next line after 60 seconds; here you can stay on a line until you finish all the calculations.

Experiment: Uchida-Kraepelin Psycho Diagnostic Test

→ 5 7 8 6 5 4 9 6 8 5 3 4 8 9 4 7 3 5 8 7 6 9 3 6
6 5 4 7 8 6 3 8 4 9 7 4 6 8 7 6 5 3 9 8 3 6 7 8
9 7 6 8 4 5 7 9 3 8 4 7 6 5 3 8 6 9 4 6 8 5 4 7
8 3 4 7 6 9 5 3 8 7 4 5 8 9 4 8 5 7 3 9 6 3 8 6
8 7 5 9 4 3 5 7 8 6 5 7 3 8 6 9 5 6 4 7 6 5 3 8
7 4 8 9 5 4 7 8 6 3 8 5 9 6 4 8 7 5 8 3 7 6 9 3
9 6 8 5 3 8 4 9 7 5 4 8 9 3 6 7 8 5 7 6 3 8 7 4
5 9 6 3 8 4 6 5 8 7 5 9 6 8 5 4 7 3 9 8 6 7 4 5
3 5 8 7 6 8 9 4 6 7 4 3 8 5 7 9 6 4 7 6 8 3 7 8
6 3 8 6 9 5 4 7 8 3 6 8 4 9 7 5 3 8 7 4 3 9 6 5
4 9 3 8 7 3 5 9 6 8 4 6 5 7 8 6 7 4 9 3 5 6 8 7
7 6 8 7 3 8 5 6 9 3 4 7 8 6 4 8 7 5 8 9 4 3 8 4
8 7 5 3 8 6 9 3 6 8 5 6 4 9 6 7 5 4 8 3 7 9 4 5
8 4 9 7 6 4 8 7 5 4 7 8 6 5 7 3 6 8 9 3 5 8 7 4
3 7 5 8 9 3 6 7 4 9 8 5 7 3 9 6 4 8 7 5 6 9 4 7
5 6 8 7 5 3 8 4 9 6 7 8 6 5 4 7 6 9 4 5 7 8 9 3
7 3 8 6 7 4 9 8 5 7 3 8 9 4 6 8 3 5 9 7 4 3 8 6

Acknowledgments: Psycho Technological Institute of Japan, Inc.

What happens in the brain when you read or listen?

Every day you do things like read books or listen to friends talking. What does the brain do at such times?

I guess you figure you can see thanks to the eyes, and hear thanks to the ears, and that's about it. In fact, we can only see and listen thanks to the brain.

The eye works like a camera. What we see passes through the lens of the eye. The image hits the retina at the back of the eye, which acts like film. The eye cannot know whether what you see is a letter, a thing, someone's face, what color it is, or anything else. That's the job of the brain.

The ear can collect sounds and send them to the brain. However, the ear cannot know whether what you listen is language, music, or some other sound. That too is the job of the brain.

So what exactly happens in the brain when you read or hear? I used myself as a test subject to find out. This chapter is all about my brain. Although it feels like I am taking off all my clothes, I am going to reveal my brain for you to see.

Reading

Let's examine how the brain works when you read in a native and a foreign language. Clever readers! You will certainly have an opportunity to learn a foreign language in the future. It is a wonderful thing to communicate and share your feelings and opinions with people around the world. So don't study because you have to, or just to get a good mark on a test, but because speaking a foreign language is an important tool for communication.

A text about world affairs written by a journalist in two languages was chosen for this experiment. The text of the foreign language is especially difficult and vague. The figures on the left show brain activity while reading.

Experiment:
Read silently in your native language and a foreign language

The areas in red are where the brain is working hard. You can see that both hemispheres of the brain are hard at work. The brain in your head is working the same way while

Chapter 2

 W hat happens in the brain when you read or listen?

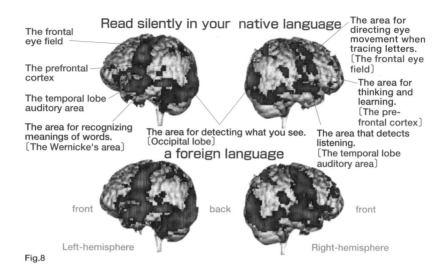

Read silently in your native language

The frontal eye field

The prefrontal cortex

The temporal lobe auditory area

The area for recognizing meanings of words. [The Wernicke's area]

The area for detecting what you see. [Occipital lobe]

a foreign language

The area for directing eye movement when tracing letters. [The frontal eye field]

The area for thinking and learning. [The prefrontal cortex]

The area that detects listening. [The temporal lobe auditory area]

front   back   front

Left-hemisphere   Right-hemisphere

Fig.8

you are reading this book right now. I'll explain step by step.

First, you recognize letters thanks to the area of your brain that detects what you see while reading. Second, you trace the letters with your eyes using the area of your brain that directs eye movement. And then, you appreciate the book thanks to the area for thinking and learning.

Interestingly enough, the area that detects listening is active at the same time even though you are not reading aloud. That's because when you are reading silently, this area is also working while you are think-

ing and learning. This area is the most important part of the brain.

How does the brain work while you are reading your native and a foreign language? First of all, almost the same areas are active for both languages. Also, both hemispheres are active. Although I've heard it said that a native language stimulates the left hemisphere and foreign languages stimulate the right, the brain is not that simple. On the other hand, you can see broader areas of activity while reading a foreign language. The right hemisphere is especially active. This means that the brain is more active while reading a foreign language. I can easily read a book in Japanese, and often read research papers written in English. However when it comes to English, I cannot help thinking about the meaning of the words and the structure of the sentences I am reading. That's why the brain is more active with a foreign language. Now, what about reading aloud?

Experiment:
Read aloud in your native language and a foreign language

Fig.9 shows us the state of the brain. The active areas are broader while reading aloud than reading silently. Especially active are the areas for thinking, learning and recognizing the meaning of words. I have done a lot of research and many experiments on brain activity and I have found that reading aloud produces the most activity. This is very surprising to me. You often read a textbook aloud in your class, don't you? Even though I realized the importance of reading aloud, I was surprised that such a broad area of the brain was active. The two experiments so far showed us that

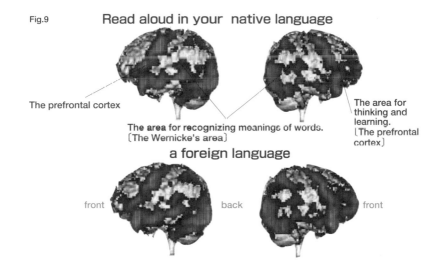

Fig.9   **Read aloud in your native language**

The prefrontal cortex

The area for recognizing meanings of words.
〔The Wernicke's area〕

The area for thinking and learning.
〔The prefrontal cortex〕

a foreign language

front   back   front

Chapter 2
What happens in the brain when you read or listen?

the brain worked hard while reading. They proved scientifically that reading, especially reading aloud, is extremely useful for training the brain. Didn't your father, mother and teachers tell you to read a lot? Down the ages we humans have somehow understood the importance of reading. How about you? Try not to feel that reading is boring. Instead, little by little try to make a habit of reading every day. I believe even a comic book can help you if you read thoughtfully. Now I hear you say "Wow, reading words on the TV display while playing a game is good, too." Unfortunately, that's not the case. Unlike a book, there are many images and sounds flowing from the display. Although I have not confirmed it by experiment, the brain probably spends more time on detecting sounds and recognizing images than on reading. As a result, we cannot expect the same kind of brain activity as when reading a book. Therefore, I still recommend that you read as much as possible.

When I was a junior high school student I used to spend a lot of time reading books unrelated to my school subjects. My parents kept some of their books in my room, and I used to pick them up and pretend to be studying. Once I found an interesting book, I tried to look for books by the same author. I dreamed I would be a writer someday. I wanted to write amusing and interesting stories that would be introduced on a midnight radio show. That was how I started dreaming to be a writer. Although I know the importance of reading thanks to my experiments, I can only read newspapers and research papers written by other researchers. Unfortunately, I am too busy with my work to read my favorite books.

Speaking of my parents' books, my father was a medical researcher, so there were many medical books in my house. I wanted to show them off to my friends. My friends and I studied photographs of anatomy subjects and cross sectional diagrams of the human body. We wanted to learn about the human body. I wasn't interested in becoming a doctor at the time, but I was good at biology and physics, so I was attracted to medicine and nature later.

Listening

Let's look at the activity of the brain when listening to someone talking. In this experiment we used a cassette tape for learning a foreign language. Fig.10 shows the differences when you listen to an easy phrase like "Where is the bus stop?" in your native language and in a foreign language.

Experiment: Listen to a conversation in your native language and a foreign language

Almost the same areas of the brain are active when listening to a conversation in your native and a foreign language. When you listen to a conversation in your native language your occipital lobe is more

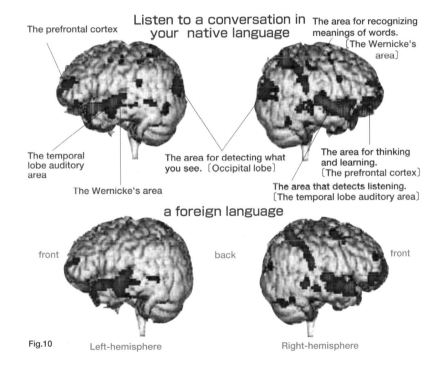

Listen to a conversation in your native language

The prefrontal cortex

The area for recognizing meanings of words. [The Wernicke's area]

The temporal lobe auditory area

The area for detecting what you see. [Occipital lobe]

The Wernicke's area

The area for thinking and learning. [The prefrontal cortex]

The area that detects listening. [The temporal lobe auditory area]

a foreign language

front   back   front

Fig.10   Left-hemisphere   Right-hemisphere

Chapter 2

What happens in the brain when you read or listen?

active. This is the area that detects what you see. Words that are heard with your ears can be seen in your brain. As the result of the experiment, we found that both hemispheres are active when listening to both native and foreign language conversations. It is commonly argued that a foreign language works the right hemisphere of the brain, and a native language works the left, but that is absolutely false. In addition, the area for thinking and learning is also active. I have already referred to this area many times, so you must be wondering "What is it?" I will tell you very soon. Incidentally listening to music is one of the things we do with our ears. Does music relax you? Does it make you feel excited or sad? How does the brain work while listening to music? Is it different from listening to speech? I chose classical and pop music for an experiment. As you know, classical music has no words. On the other hand, pop music uses words to convey a message from the singer to the listeners. Does brain activity differ depending on whether there are words or not?

Experiment: Listen to classical and pop music

Unlike the state of the brain when you listen to speech, only a small area is active when you listen to music. Only the area of the brain that governs listening is active. To say that listening to music is relaxing is to say that the majority of the brain is in a relaxed state. The right hemisphere of the brain is active when listening to the melody or tones, while the left hemisphere is active when listening to speech. Thus, unlike the many areas in use for conversation, when listening to music only the area for detecting sounds is working hard. I think many of you listen to music while studying. Once you learn the results of the experiment you may be relieved and say, "It's OK to listen to music while studying because it uses a different area of the brain." Certainly, since music can ease stress it can improve the atmosphere for studying. On the other hand, if you think about the meaning of the words and sing along, it's better not to listen to music while studying. If you try to listen to a conversation on TV or

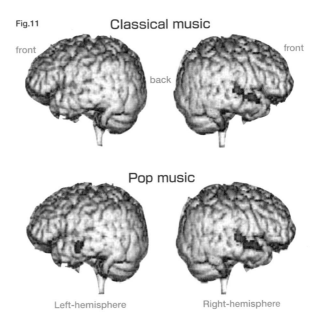

Fig.11

Classical music

front

back

front

Pop music

Left-hemisphere

Right-hemisphere

the radio, regardless of whether it is in your native language or a foreign language, a broader area of the brain becomes active. This includes the area that governs studying. In other words, it is probably better not to study while the radio or tele vision are turned on, since this will interfere with the activity of the brain needed for studying. This theory can be confirmed by the following experiment which you can carry out yourself.

Procedure
1. Prepare a stopwatch.
2. There are three sets of problems, one addition, one subtraction and one multiplication, on pages40-41. Each set has three columns of 15 problems. Choose one column from each set and solve out loud as quickly as possible. Ask someone to clock your time.
3. Next, change the conditions: Turn on the TV. Listen carefully to the TV and then repeat step 2 above, with the same problems.

Chapter 2

What happens in the brain when you read or listen?

Which was faster, the first or second try? Since you solved the same problems, maybe you thought the second try would be faster. What was your result? I'll bet many of you did better on the first try. Now you can understand why TV interferes with the activity of the brain needed for studying. If you did better the second time, can you remember what the TV program was about? You didn't really pay attention, did you? The brain actually blocked out the TV to allow you to calculate. Incidentally, when I write papers I usually use ear plugs to stop sounds from interfering with my brain activity. This helps me to concentrate and speeds up my work.

The most important place in the brain

When you read and listen to your native language or a foreign language, the area of the brain that governs thinking and learning becomes active. You have seen the figure on page 13 illustrating brain activity when a 7th grade student was doing single digit arithmetic. In this experiment the same area of the brain for thinking and learning was active. It is located just behind your forehead and is called the "prefrontal cortex" in brain science. The brain is often compared to a computer. If the brain is a computer, the prefrontal cortex is important enough to say that it's the computer inside the computer. It performs the highest functions of the brain. The prefrontal cortex works like a control tower. It issues the order to think, to memorize; it produces emotions, such as pleasure, anger and sorrow, and the motivation to do things. These, and more, are all the work of the prefrontal cortex.

Compared with apes humans have a large and well-developed prefrontal cortex. It is the large prefrontal cortex that distinguishes humans from other animals. It can be said that the prefrontal cortex is the most important part of the brain. Therefore, it is very important for us to train it and keep it active.

In this book we are going to be talking a lot about the prefrontal cortex and its functions. It's a strange name and sounds difficult, but please keep it in mind.

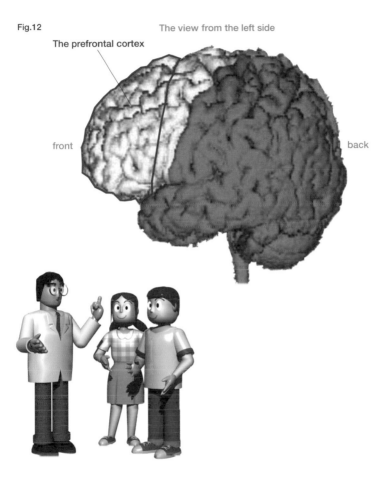

Fig.12   The view from the left side

The prefrontal cortex

front   back

Chapter 2

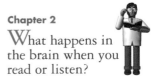

What happens in
the brain when you
read or listen?

25

Chapter 2: Putting it all together

Reading:

● Many parts of both sides of the brain are active while reading.

● The prefrontal cortex, the most important place in the brain for thinking and learning, is active, too.

● When you read either a native or a foreign language, both sides of the brain are active.

● The brain is more active when you read aloud than silently.

Listening:

● When you listen to a conversation, many parts of both sides of the brain are active.

● Both hemispheres are active when listening to both native and foreign language conversations.

● When listening to music, only the areas for detecting sounds are working intensively.

Understanding more about the brain —2
The human and the animal brain

Please compare the size of the human brain to that of other animals. Cats, beavers, anteaters and squirrel monkeys all have simple, small and wrinkle-free brains. Even a chimpanzee's brain, which is similar to ours, is smaller and has fewer wrinkles. Can you find any other differences besides size? As I explained in this chapter, you can see that the human prefrontal cortex is large and well-developed. By the way a dolphin's brain is larger and more wrinkled than ours. Therefore they can communicate with each other using a quasi-language. They are probably saying, "These horrible human beings are polluting our world, the sea" or "I am me, not another dolphin," just like you say "I am me, not another person."

Comparison of brain sizes

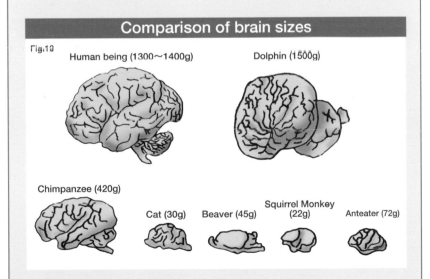

Fig.10

Human being (1300~1400g)

Dolphin (1500g)

Chimpanzee (420g)

Cat (30g)

Beaver (45g)

Squirrel Monkey (22g)

Anteater (72g)

Let's try 2

You can practice my experiments by following these instructions. Even without using special equipment, your brain will work the same as explained on page 18 and 19.

Experiment: Read in your native language (English) and a foreign language (Japanese).

1. "I want this chair. How much is it?" "It's 150 dollars. It's a nice chair."

"Watashi wa, konoisu ga hosii. Ikura desuka?" "Hyakugojyuu doru desu. Sutekina isudesu."

2. "What sports do you like, Dave?"
"I like cycling and tennis. How about you, Bob?"
"I like volleyball."

"Anatawa, dono supoutsuga sukidesuka, Deibu?"
"Watashiwa saikuringu to tenisu ga sukidesu.Anatawa doudesuka, bobu?"   "Watashiwa bareibouru ga sukidesu."

●How to do it:
1. Read the English silently.
2. The Japanese sentences are translated from the English. Read them silently. If you cannot understand the Japanese at all, please ask your parents or a teacher to teach you how to read it. Now please read the English aloud.
3. Read the Japanese aloud.

3. "Hello." "Hello, this is Alice. Is John there?"
"No, he's studying at the library."

"Moshimoshi "
"Moshimoshi, arisu desu. Jon wa imasuka?"
"Iie, kare wa toshokan de benkyou shiteimasu."

4. "Can I help you?"
"I want these oranges and cherries."
"That will be 900 yen."

"Naniwo, sashiage mashouka?"
"Watashiwa, orenji to sakuranbou ga hoshiinodesuga."
"Kyuuhyaku en ni narimasu."

Chapter 2
What happens in the brain when you read or listen?

Chapter 3

Don't mock
calculations!

At the beginning of this book I talked about experiments that investigated brain activity while playing computer games, and during a test of single digit addition. With a little mischief in mind, I thought up this experiment when I was in graduate school at Tohoku University.

After I graduated from Tohoku University, I went to graduate school to study brain science. However, there were no teachers specializing in the study of brain activity. Completely at a loss about what to do next, I finally decided to study at the Primate Research Institute of Kyoto University.

At the Primate Research Institute, I studied the brain activity of apes under the supervision of Professor Kisou Kubota, a top authority on brain science. Professor Kubota taught me not only about research, but also the attitude of a researcher.

At that time I came across a paper written by Professor Roland, a Swedish researcher. It was a paper on experiments using imaging to see what the brain does when we feel, think or get excited about something. It was exactly the research I wanted to do! I immediately wrote a letter expressing my strong desire to do research under him.

While I was waiting for a reply from Prof. Roland, I conducted the experiments on calculation and computer games at Tohoku University graduate school.

Finally an answer came: "Come to Sweden." And I was off to Sweden to study brain science with Prof. Roland. I learned from the professor how to write a paper, what it meant to be a researcher, and so many other things. Even now as I start work every morning at 7:00, I often recall such lessons as: "Get to the lab in the morning before everyone else, and finish your work before the others arrive."

Meeting Prof. Kubota and Prof. Roland truly changed my life. I am doing brain science now thanks to them. I hope all of you will have a chance to meet someone who will have such a powerful impact on you. Be sure to grab the chance when it comes.

After two years of research in Sweden, I returned to Japan, and embarked on various experiments and research projects.

One of these was to confirm what

Chapter 3

Don't mock calculations!

exactly the brain does during simple calculation.

The Magical Power of Simple Calculation

Do you remember the results of the experiment we looked at before? We learned more parts of our brain are active when carrying out simple calculation than when playing computer games. Weren't you surprised by this result? You must have thought playing a computer game used your head and body for all they were worth! I thought so too! In fact, I was so shocked I couldn't accept the results. How could such a boring task like calculating activate(s) so many parts of the brain? I thought something had to be wrong. I had conducted the experiment with only five college students. Maybe the results would be different if I examined more people and various types of calculating. If I did the experiments again, maybe I could get a more detailed explanation of how the brain worked.

I decided to examine brain activity during subtraction and multiplication as well as single digit addition. The subject had to solve problems such as 2+5, 7−3, and 8×9 that were projected on a screen once for 2 seconds. Since the calculations were easy, college, junior high, and elementary school students were included in the experiments. I thought the problems were so easy that the brain wouldn't have to work very hard. That said...

Experiment: Do simple calculation

Fig.14 shows the results from ten college students.

When the experiment using simple calculation was carried out, it was confirmed that various places in both hemispheres of the brain were active. We also confirmed that generally the same areas were used regardless of whether the calculation was subtraction, multiplication or addition.

However, please note that the area for speaking was also active during multiplication. Why is language required for calculating? Can you guess? How do you solve problems like 4×4, 8×8? That's right: You

Fig.14

Simple calculation

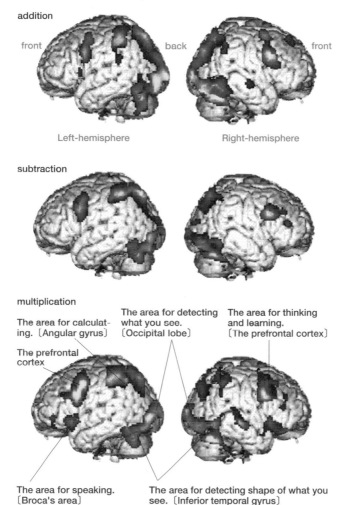

addition

front   back   front

Left-hemisphere   Right-hemisphere

subtraction

multiplication

The area for calculating. [Angular gyrus]

The area for detecting what you see. [Occipital lobe]

The area for thinking and learning. [The prefrontal cortex]

The prefrontal cortex

The area for speaking. [Broca's area]

The area for detecting shape of what you see. [Inferior temporal gyrus]

Chapter 3

Don't mock calculations!

use the multiplication table. You learned single digit multiplication by memorizing the tables, didn't you? Therefore the area related to words is activated. Checking the results I was surprised at another finding. The prefrontal cortex, the area for thinking and learning, of both hemispheres is active during simple calculation. Dealing with numbers is an important and sophisticated activity for human beings. As a matter of fact, except for some chimps trained by humans to handle numbers, only human beings can calculate. Can humans calculate because the prefrontal cortex is large and well-developed? Or has the prefrontal cortex grown and developed because humans can calculate? This is like "Which came first, the chicken or the egg?" Whichever came first, I am sure you can appreciate how important calculating is for our brain. On page 13 you learned about brain activity while a 7th grade student was calculating. We did the same experiment with primary school students. Generally the same areas of the brain were active as in high school and college students. From primary school to college, simple calculation triggers brain activity. As you have seen, calculation is extremely helpful in training and developing your brain. If you think simple calculation is useless, think again. And here is another suggestion: Before studying something difficult, do a little calculating for just a minute or two. You will be able to study more efficiently because various parts of your brain will be activated. It's like warming up the engine before using a car.

What happens when you solve complex calculations?

Next, let's see what the brain does when doing complex calculations; for example $54 \div (0.51 - 0.19)$. The average college student can solve this kind of problem in under a minute. Try it yourself. Did you get the correct answer? Although it seems difficult, it's just a combination of division and subtraction. Do you think the same areas of the brain are activated as for simple calculation?

Experiment:
Do complex calculation

Nine college students were the subjects for this experiment. What a result! The right hemisphere is not working at all! Only the left side is working. I was shocked at the results. I thought the brain would work harder solving complex calculations, but it was the opposite. I have been surprised many times by the interesting results of experiments. Obtaining unexpected results and finding out why is one of the great pleasures of studying brain science. This is what I think about the results: You can quickly answer 2+3 equals 5, can't you? But can you answer $54 \div (0.51 - 0.19)$ quickly? You probably say to yourself, "First, 0.51 minus 0.19 is 0.32, then to solve $54 \div 0.32$ multiply by 100, and so on ..." Well, thanks to the work of many scientists we know that the area that produces language is located in the left hemisphere if a person is right-handed. Since all the subjects were right-handed, the left side of the brain was active while the subjects talked to themselves. When a person does complex calculations, the prefrontal cortex for thinking and learning works hard alongside the area that produces language.

Fig.15

Complex calculation

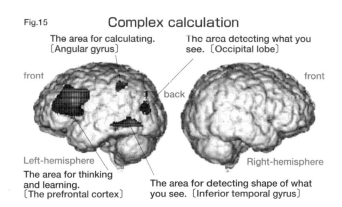

The area for calculating. [Angular gyrus]

The area detecting what you see. [Occipital lobe]

front

back

front

Left-hemisphere

Right-hemisphere

The area for thinking and learning. [The prefrontal cortex]

The area for detecting shape of what you see. [Inferior temporal gyrus]

Chapter 3

Don't mock calculations!

What happens when you solve word problems?

I investigated brain activity while solving word problems; for example: "After receiving some pencils from her mother Aya has 48% more pencils. If she now has 37 pencils, how many did she have originally?"

Experiment: Solve word problems

You can see that the left side of the brain is active. The active area is located in the prefrontal cortex, but it's slightly broader than the area for complex calculations. The process for solving word problems is first, understand the problem by reading it repeatedly, then make an expression, and then go over it in your head. This activates the area for thinking and learning as well. What a result! The area for calculating is not working at all! I believe this is because the brain is working hard to come up with an expression.

Now, I have a piece of advice for you about how to learn arithmetic and mathematics. Since the areas in the brain for complex calculations and word problems are almost the same, if you are not good at word problems, try doing more calculating. You can train your brain and

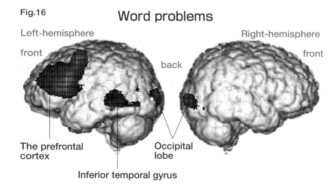

Fig.16   **Word problems**

Left-hemisphere   Right-hemisphere

front   back   front

The prefrontal cortex   Occipital lobe

Inferior temporal gyrus

improve your word problem skills at the same time. The area for producing language is active when solving complex calculations and word problems. I think studying your native language can also improve your arithmetic, math and other subjects. Remember the prefrontal cortex for thinking is active while reading aloud. Therefore, it's a good idea to read aloud when you solve difficult word problems. It might help you solve problems more easily. Of course, if you are not alone, you will have to lower your voice!

Chapter 3: Putting it all together

- Many parts of both sides of the brain are active while carrying out simple calculations.
- The active area is located in the left side of the brain when solving complex calculations and word problems, but the word problem area is slightly broader than the area for complex calculations.
- When you do complex calculations and word problems, the area for producing words is active.
- When you do complex calculations and word problems, the prefrontal cortex, the most important place in the brain for thinking and learning, is active.

Chapter 3

Don't mock calculations!

Understanding more about the brain —3
Four rooms of the cerebrum
. . . .

   If you have read this book up to here, you know that our brain doesn't work as a chunk. Our brain contains the cerebrum, cerebellum and brain stem. The cerebrum has four parts: the front, back, top and side. Each part has its own function.

   The frontal lobe is located inside of the forehead and performs the important function of controlling movement (motor area). Broca's area, which produces words and the prefrontal cortex, which performs the most important roles, are located here as well.

   The parietal lobe is located at the top of the brain. One important function of the parietal lobe is sensing what you are touching (sensory area). Detecting location and direction with respect to your surroundings (parietal association area) and calculation (angular gyrus) are located here as well.

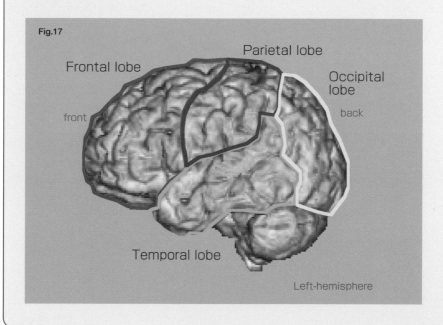

Fig.17

Parietal lobe

Frontal lobe

Occipital lobe

front

back

Temporal lobe

Left-hemisphere

The occipital lobe, located at the back of the brain, controls images (visual area). What you see is transmitted to this area and processed.

The temporal lobe located at the side of the brain and inside of the ear is for detecting what you hear (auditory area). Detecting the shape of things you see (inferior temporal gyrus) is also located here. The language comprehension area (Wernicke's area) is in the layered area of the temporal and parietal lobes.

Fig.18

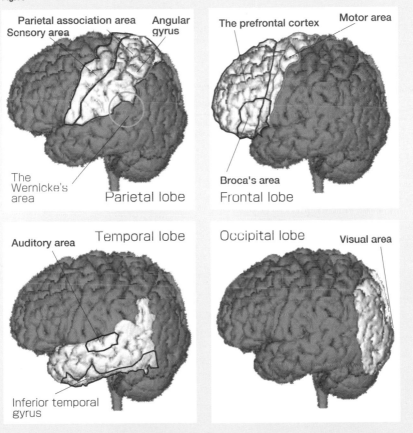

Let's try 3

You can practice my experiments by following these instructions. Even without using special equipment, your brain will work the same as explained on page33.

Experiment: Carry out single digit addition, subtraction and multiplication.

4 + 2	6 + 8	1 + 2	3 - 1	8 - 3	8 - 2
8 + 2	4 + 5	9 + 2	8 - 5	5 - 3	6 - 1
5 + 5	7 + 1	7 + 6	6 - 3	6 - 2	5 - 4
7 + 5	3 + 5	2 + 4	7 - 6	7 - 5	7 - 2
3 + 6	1 + 1	6 + 6	2 - 1	3 - 2	9 - 9
7 + 4	5 + 7	4 + 9	9 - 7	5 - 1	4 - 4
8 + 9	8 + 4	9 + 3	4 - 2	4 - 4	8 - 8
5 + 8	2 + 8	1 + 6	5 - 2	7 - 3	9 - 4
2 + 3	5 + 1	8 + 5	5 - 5	8 - 1	2 - 2
6 + 7	9 + 7	3 + 7	7 - 4	9 - 5	9 - 3
9 + 9	6 + 5	5 + 2	8 - 4	6 - 6	7 - 1
1 + 9	1 + 7	3 + 1	8 - 6	4 - 1	7 - 7
4 + 1	8 + 8	7 + 9	1 - 1	3 - 3	8 - 4
5 + 3	4 + 7	6 + 3	4 - 3	8 - 6	3 - 2
2 + 7	6 + 1	9 + 4	9 - 1	9 - 8	5 - 4

●How to do it:
1. Cover the problems with a piece of paper.
2. Move the paper to solve the problems one by one.
3. Just answer mentally. You don't have to write anything down.
4. Solve at the pace of one problem per two seconds.

3 × 7	3 × 8	8 × 7
4 × 8	4 × 4	1 × 3
5 × 1	7 × 2	2 × 9
2 × 7	2 × 7	5 × 6
9 × 4	6 × 3	2 × 3
6 × 2	9 × 9	7 × 8
7 × 7	8 × 6	8 × 9
8 × 3	2 × 4	7 × 9
3 × 9	6 × 8	9 × 3
6 × 6	7 × 7	3 × 6
2 × 6	4 × 5	4 × 9
8 × 8	6 × 1	7 × 1
5 × 9	4 × 7	2 × 8
7 × 3	5 × 4	6 × 7
9 × 1	6 × 9	5 × 8

Chapter 3

Don't mock
calculations!

Food for the brain: Train your brain by studying every day

Maybe some of you are thinking, "If I wasn't born with smarts, it'd be no use trying" or "I don't have to study; my parents are smart so I will be, too." If that is how you are thinking, you are seriously mistaken. If you spend a few days without exercising, your muscles will get weaker. Likewise your brain will become weaker without exercise. On the contrary, everyone can train his or her brain by learning properly. As a matter of fact, like your body, your brain is developing day by day.

What is the best way of learning? I can hear you saying "If there's a way, please tell me." Unfortunately we are still waiting to find the complete answer. However, in the meantime, I have some helpful advice based on brain science on how to be a more efficient learner. From primary to high school I was never fond of studying, but if I had known about what I am about to tell you, I would have learned more. You still have enough time to catch up! Let your brain teach you how to be a more efficient learner.

What does "physical learning" mean?

We usually think of "learning" as knowing how to solve problems, get skills and remember what we studied at school and at home. At the same time, we also think of "learning" as knowing how to ride a bicycle or practicing spinning on the horizontal bar. Here are some interesting results from an experiment in "physical learning."

Experiment:
Look at the world at a 60-degree angle

Look at Fig.19. The college student subject is allowed to see only via a camera. The camera is then

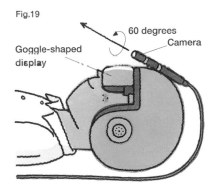

Fig.19

Goggle-shaped display

60 degrees
Camera

Chapter 4

Food for the brain: Train your brain by studying every day

turned 60 degrees clockwise. That's to say, the world is viewed by the subject at a 60-degree angle from normal. Although the angle happened to be 60 degrees because of the equipment we used, whatever the angle, the world would still look very, very different.

I also tried this experiment on myself. It felt very strange. Although I could see my own arms and hands, it was as if they were not mine. I couldn't move them the way I wanted to.

Fig.20

When we started the experiment.

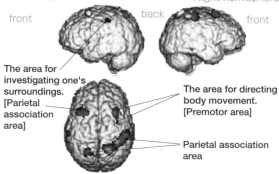

Left-hemisphere

Right-hemisphere

front   back   front

The area for investigating one's surroundings. [Parietal association area]

The area for directing body movement. [Premotor area]

Parietal association area

When you can move your arms properly.

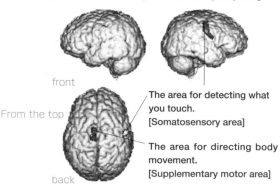

front

From the top

back

The area for detecting what you touch. [Somatosensory area]

The area for directing body movement. [Supplementary motor area]

I was totally confused about how to move my arms. After trying various ways to move them for a long time, I was finally able to do so, but the movements were jerky. I felt as if I had managed to solve an unbelievably difficult problem. What was going on in my brain?

You can see a summary of the results with six right-handed college students. The figure "When we started the experiment" shows the brain when the subjects were confused about how to move their arms. Various areas in both hemispheres are active. The colored areas in the upper part of the brain that are active are associated with investigating one's surroundings. Trying to adjust to an unfamiliar world, the brain activates various areas. After various adjustments you can move your arms properly as the areas of the brain for directing body movement and touch kick in. The brain learns through the physical body by testing out various approaches. That's how something you practice repeatedly becomes automatic.

To complete the experiment the inclined camera is returned to the normal position. What happens next? Will the same confusion occur? No. Interestingly enough, your body remembers. The adjustments made for the unfamiliar world disappear instantly. The results of the experiment teach us three things:

1. Various areas of the brain are activated when you start learning something.
2. As learning progresses the amount of brain activity decreases.
3. When you stop learning, everything goes back to the way it was.

The brain is like a mosaic

Let me explain the mechanism of the brain by comparing it to something familiar.

Have you ever seen a mosaic picture? From far away it looks like a single object, but if you look at it up close you can see it is made up of many tiny pieces. The brain is similar in that it is made of many tiny brain cells. All the cells in the brain are linked to each other. Unlike humans who have just two hands, brain cells have ten, even twenty "hands" that can be easily linked together.

Why do they need to be linked?

Chapter 4

Food for the brain: Train your brain by studying every day

Imagine you and your classmates are in a circle holding hands. When you feel your hand being squeezed by the person to your right, you squeeze the hand of the person to your left. I start by squeezing the hand of the person to my left, and this is immediately passed on down the line. The brain sends information in the same way, from the first cell to the last cell. It's something like playing the "telephone" game, but in the case of the brain, the information never changes on the way. What is your depth of understanding? It is the brain activating brain cells that are linked to each other, and sending information in

this way. These are the red areas in the brain that appear in the illustration.

Build expressways in the brain by studying

Please keep the previous experiment in mind. When we inclined the camera 60 degrees, the subject was confused and various areas of the brain were activated. At that time the brain was trying to escape confusion in various ways by deciding which cell should link to which to pass the information on.

Despite making many detours, in

Fig.21

the end the brain found the first cell and the last cell. (This process is shown in Fig22, ①.)

By sending information repeatedly, the brain soon finds the shortest path from the first to the last cell. Therefore the amount of brain activity decreases. This is the moment the subject suddenly feels he can move his arms at will. (This process is shown in Fig22, ②.)

Remember that if you stop the experiment here, what the body has remembered instantly disappears. The path is still narrow, but like an old country road, if there isn't enough traffic, weeds cover it, and soon no one can use it. By learning

repeatedly and passing information among the brain's cells frequently, we keep the brain active and the paths open. Instead of a country road, we can build expressways that can go everywhere and in every direction. (This process is shown in Fig22, ③.). This is what I mean when I say "Train your brain."

Once you have built these expressways in your brain, you will never forget what you have learned. As a matter of fact, "physical learning" and "mental learning" are exactly the same activity for the brain. Therefore the results of the experiment can be applied to "mental learning."

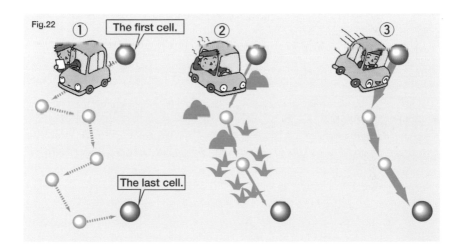

Fig.22 ① The first cell. ② ③
The last cell.

That's to say, by repeatedly and frequently passing information among the brain's cells, studying is the only way to change a country road into an expressway. This is my point in emphasizing in this book the importance of having an active brain.

You can train and develop your brain most efficiently up until you are twenty years old. This means that your time in school is the time for building expressways and training your brain. Even so, please don't misunderstand me. I don't mean you stop learning after you are twenty; you can still build expressways.

When I was in high school I didn't study hard. I only started studying hard to get into college and to study medicine, but I have continued to study ever since I entered the field of brain science. With effort, you can build expressways no matter how old you are.

As far as learning efficiency is concerned, there is a strong relationship between your age and the amount you can learn and develop your brain. The human body is fully developed by about the age of twenty. Therefore your brain develops and builds many expressways up until you are twenty years old. How lucky you are!

Keep your brain active

In order to improve the brain, we need to build many expressways by activating the brain as much as possible. As we have seen in the experiments in Chapters 2 and 3, the brain is extremely active while reading and calculating. Studying at school and at home is the most efficient way to build many expressways. Now, I would like to tell you about what we have confirmed by experiment about brain activities related to learning other than reading and calculating.

(1) Memorizing

Memorizing is an important learning activity. According to the results of experiments done on brain activity during memorizing, the prefrontal cortex is active in issuing the command to memorize. The brain has different places for storing various sorts of memories; such as: sentences and formulas, the shape and location of objects, people's faces, names and so on.

Therefore various parts of the brain are activated when memorizing various sorts of things.

(2) The knack for memorizing

I am getting off the subject a bit, but let me say a little about memory here.

You make a phone call immediately after hearing a number without writing it down. It's easy to remember the number while you are making the call. But if you stop and chat for a moment just before making the call, what happens? You forget the number just after making the call, don't you?

Five to nine digits can be stored as short-term memory, and remembered for several minutes at most. This fact was confirmed by psychologists 100 years ago. In most countries a telephone number is seven or eight digits at most, without the area code. I guess you are wondering if you can memorize a number with more than ten digits. Don't worry. You can. You never forget your home or your friends' telephone numbers, do you? Words and letters are the same. Now you got it. In order to hang on to a memory you must memorize it

repeatedly. You build an expressway from the command area to the memory pick-up area where the memory is stored in your brain. Utilizing a combination of sounds is helpful for memorizing. Also reading aloud and writing things down will help you to memorize. That's to say, producing words, making your eyes and ears work, and moving your body are all activities that activate the brain and help you to remember.

I used to memorize things solely by repeating them over and over again. Even if I thought I had something memorized, I tried to repeat it again. In doing so, when I couldn't remember something on a test, I could often recall the memory by association with other memories of the scene or place where I was when I was memorizing.

(3) How to use test results

When you get your test back, I am sure your teacher says something like, "Review the test, especially where you made mistakes, and think carefully about why you made a mistake and how you can correct it. Never make the same mistake twice!" I think many of

Chapter 4

Food for the brain: Train your brain by studying every day

you may only care about your score, or how many you got right or wrong. However, as a matter of fact, your teacher is giving you good advice. I will explain why with the results of the following experiment.

Experiment: Draw a line exactly 10 cm long with your eyes closed

Close your eyes and try drawing lines exactly 10 cm long. Get a friend to tell you first, only whether the lines you drew are exactly 10 cm or not, and second, whether the lines you drew are 10 cm, give or take 0.5 cm. We investigated brain activity under both conditions. This experiment corresponds to two approaches to test results. The first way corresponds

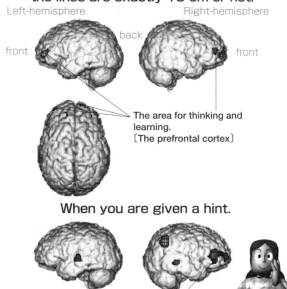

Fig.23 **When you are told only whether the lines are exactly 10 cm or not.**

Left-hemisphere   Right-hemisphere

back
front   front

The area for thinking and learning.
〔The prefrontal cortex〕

When you are given a hint.

front

The prefrontal cortex

back   From the top

to only caring about whether you got the right or wrong answer. The second way corresponds to thinking about why you made a mistake and how to correct it.

Try the same experiment yourself (see how on page56). You will find it very difficult to draw a line exactly 10 cm long.

Look at Fig.23 on page50. The brain is more active when you are given a hint about whether you are off by plus or minus 0.5 centimeter than if you are told the line drawn is exactly 10cm or not. The prefrontal cortex in the right hemisphere is especially active. Since it is the area of the brain for thinking, the prefrontal cortex is trying through trial and error to draw a line just the right length by using the hints.

I am sure you understand now. When you review your test results, please think about the reasons for your mistakes by getting some feedback on the right answers. In so doing your prefrontal cortex will work harder.

Study methods for building a better and stronger brain

To conclude this chapter, I have put together a rundown of efficient ways to build a better and stronger brain based on the results of experiments and brain science research.

(1) Before studying

①Don't study when you feel hungry.

We humans ingest food, and convert it into a sugar called glucose. Our body cells consume that glucose. According to investigations on the distribution of glucose in the body, the brain is the biggest consumer of glucose. As a matter of fact, the brain consumes only glucose and oxygen. Insufficient glucose causes the brain to malfunction and no glucose can cause brain death in an instant. Therefore please eat well before studying. Don't overeat or study immediately after eating. I recommend that you rest at least thirty minutes after eating in order to digest well. It's also a good idea to rest rather than run around after lunch at school.

②Establish a good environment for concentrating on studying.

I mentioned that it's not good to listen to conversations, watch TV or listen to the radio while studying since the brain gets busy doing a lot of things unrelated to learning. If you feel uneasy about some-

Chapter 4

Food for the brain: Train your brain by studying every day

thing, take care of it before you sit down to study. Your brain is most active when you are thinking "positively."

③Get a good night's sleep every day.

When you feel sleepy, it means your brain is tired. Sleep well and stay fresh; otherwise, your brain will not be able to work well. Never stay up late!

(2) While studying

①Understand what you are studying and put it in its proper place.

Everybody learns new things by groping around at first. The brain must grope around, too. At such times the brain is busy trying to build paths from one cell to another. Don't give up! Continue studying until your brain establishes the expressway for efficient learning. I know it's hard to tough it out, but you need to make an effort to understand and solve the problems you run into. One effective method is to think about the relationship between what you are studying now and what you have studied before, and put it in its proper place.

②Study over and over again.

It's easy to soon forget what you have learned if you stop studying as soon as you get only the gist. Study the same subject matter over and over again to broaden and strengthen the expressways connecting the cells in your brain.

③Study well and speedily.

You can make progress easily if you build lots of broad expressways and establish a network among cells all over the brain. You can't tell if a network has been established only by how well you can handle the subject matter. If you can study both well and speedily, it means the expressway network has been established.

④Memorize many different kinds of things.

The brain has different places for storing different sorts of memory. Therefore many different places in the brain will be activated if you memorize various sorts of things. At the same time in this way you can develop a well-balanced brain.

Memorizing is a very important activity for the brain. Repetition and making associations make memorizing easy.

⑤Concentrate on studying.

I have investigated brain activity when trying to distinguish by feel the heads or tails side of a coin. Try it yourself now. Put a coin in your pocket. Can you tell by feel which side is heads or tails? Where do you look while you are feeling? Do you look at the wall or the ceiling? Do you close your eyes? The brain ignores activities that interfere with concentrating on feeling the coin. As a result, you close your eyes or look absently at something. Once the brain starts concentrating on something, it tends to ignore other activities. Therefore if you concentrate on studying, you can make good progress.

⑥Study every day.

You need to train your brain to create a keen brain. You know how to train your body. If you eat right and exercise every day your body will become strong. The same is true for the brain. Study is exercise and food for the brain. By studying every day the brain gets food and exercises various areas, developing a stronger brain.

A tool chest in your head

You've read this book up to here. I can hear some of you saying, "What? Studying every day is the best method to make a keen and strong brain? I was hoping for some shortcut ... Boy, am I disappointed!" As I have shown you, this is what brain science has taught us. I suggested to you several times that you build many expressways in your brain. Another way to look at this is you need tools to think about, cut through and solve problems. However, it's not enough to only have tools; you need to use them skillfully. How do you use them skillfully? My experience is this: I lived in Maebashi, Gunma Prefecture in Japan from grade one to three in elementary school. I often enjoyed fishing and swimming in a nearby river, and I almost drowned several times. When I visited the same river later as an adult I found it was just a stream. I caught fish, played baseball in the fields, ate mulberries and even bee

Chapter 4

Food for the brain: Train your brain by studying every day

grubs; from primary to high school we kids enjoyed nature. I believe playing like that sharpened the tools in our brains. Playing with friends, thinking about and coping with various problems, making things out of what we found in nature, inventing new games, moving our bodies—all these activities forced us to use our brains. A video game doesn't do much for the brain. You play alone, and it doesn't require any creativity. Although it hasn't been proven yet, it will be someday. It is important to play and have various experiences with many kinds of people.

When you have trouble studying

Building up your tool chest and your skills requires a certain minimum investment at home and at school. Your parents and other grown-ups tell you to study hard because they know the importance of studying based on their own failures and successes. If you try reading aloud or carrying out simple calculation, and you still don't feel the brain working, don't give up. It is working. The importance of studying has been proven scientifically. Whenever you have trouble studying, please remember the message of this book, "Studying activates the brain. Through study and repetition you can create the tools you need to solve any problem you encounter in life

Chapter 4: Putting it all together

- By learning repeatedly you can keep the brain active and build the shortest information paths among the brain's cells.
- By learning repeatedly you can change the shortest paths to broader and stronger expressways.
- Developing a stronger brain means building as many expressways as possible.
- In order to develop a strong brain it is important to study and train your brain every day.
- Developing a strong brain means building up your thinking and solving tool chest.
- It's important to use your brain tools well.

Brain cells and the signaling system

In this chapter I explained brain cells and the signaling system by comparing them to something familiar. The tiny pieces of a mosaic picture are the nucleus, and the hand holding a circle of friends refers to axons. Here are some more details. Nucleuses number over several hundred billion and many axons come out from each nucleus. The axon is a "live electric wire" sending signals from the nucleus. These electric wires bind together to make extremely complex networks. As a matter of fact, brain activity means the activity of the nucleuses and axon networks. Actually a slight electric current passes from the nucleus to the axon. Therefore we can detect the electric current in your brain by using a device like a galvanometer. The electric current from the nucleus reaches a place called a "synapse." The synapse is a small gap separating neurons. Communication of information between neurons is done by moving chemicals, called "neurotransmitters," across the synapse. You can think of these chemical substances as small chemical factories attached to the nucleus.

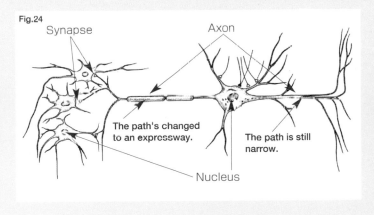

Fig.24

Synapse

Axon

The path's changed to an expressway.

The path is still narrow.

Nucleus

Chapter 4

Food for the brain:
Train your brain by
studying every day

Let's try 4

You can practice my experiments by following these instructions. Even without using special equipment, your brain will work the same as explained on page50.

Experiment: Close your eyes and try drawing lines exactly 10 cm. long.

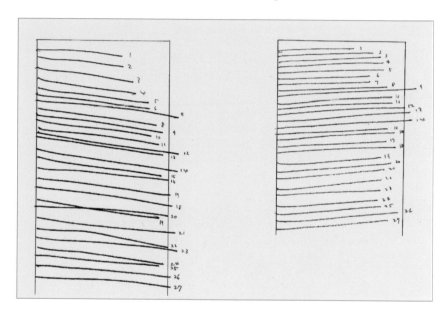

●How to do it:

1. This experiment requires two persons, you and your partner. Prepare a piece of graph paper and a pencil.

2. Draw two vertical lines 10 centimeters apart on the graph paper. The left will be the starting line and the right will be the finishing line.

3. Hold a pencil with your eyes closed. Your partner moves the tip of the pencil to the starting line.

4. Step 1: Draw lines exactly 10 centimeters long. Your partner tells you whether the line is just the right length.

5. Carry on for two minutes.

6. Step 2: Your partner tells you whether the lines you are drawing are 10 cm., give or take 0.5 cm.

7. Carry on for two minutes. How did you do?

Chapter 4

Food for the brain: Train your brain by studying every day

The brain moves your body

Do you like sports? Are you into any particular sport?

When I was small I used to do things like swimming in the river, playing tennis with my father, and playing baseball in the rice field after rice harvest. I was also very absorbed in club activities: baseball in primary school, volleyball in high school and rugby when I was in college. Whatever the sport, I still love to move my body even now. In this chapter I will talk about the relationship between the brain and exercise. You have turned pages up to this point in the book. This is the combined movement of your fingers, hands and arms. You also move your eyes to trace the letters and words in this book.

Have you ever experienced any difficulty doing these activities?

Probably not. I am sure you have been able to do all these things automatically. Nevertheless, even when we do such simple activities, the brain is as busy as a bee doing innumerable tasks.

Have you heard that you can make your brain stronger if you use your fingers a lot? Do you think it's true? Does the brain work differently if you are right or left-handed? Let's do another experiment.

The brain mechanism for moving the body

First let's look at brain activity while we are moving our bodies. Right now this book is open and you are looking at what appears on this page. Let's follow in Fig.25 the steps the brain takes to turn the

Fig.25

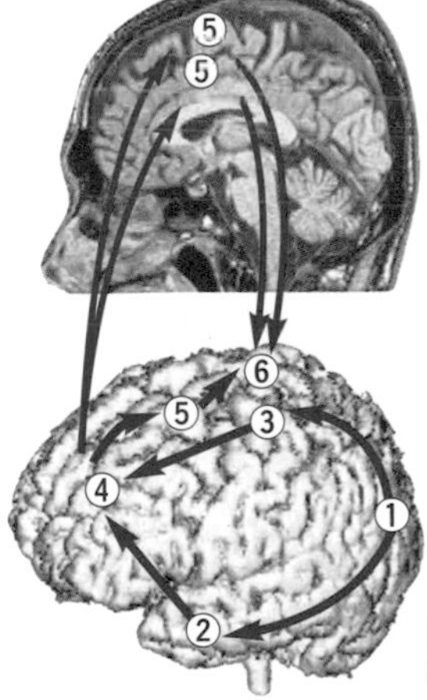

Brain activities when you turn one page and another of a book.

Inside the brain

front

back

Left-hemi-sphere

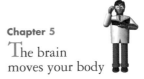

Chapter 5

The brain moves your body

pages of a book:

1. The image passing through your eyes is sent to the area (①) of the brain for perceiving what you see. Then, to investigate further, the image is sent to another two areas of the brain.

2. See the arrow going down from the back of the brain? The arrow shows the direction of movement toward the area (②) for perceiving such things as "This is the book," "These are written words," and so on.

3. Another arrow is going to the upper part of the brain. This arrow is pointing to the area (③) for distinguishing where the book is in relation to your own body.

4. In the next step, information is sent to the prefrontal cortex (④) , which controls the highest-level activities. Here the command to turn the page is issued and sent on.

5. The specific command to turn the page is produced at this point (⑤) . Based on the images passing through the eyes, the position of the book and the reading speed, the brain formulates the method and procedure for selecting the appropriate movement, along with

the order and timing.

6. Finally, the command is sent to the area (⑥) whose cells command the muscles to move. The cells order the muscles in the arms, hands and fingers to expand or contract.

In addition, the brain uses the sensing mechanism in the arms and fingers to constantly check to make sure the movements of the muscles are smooth. If the movements are not smooth, the brain changes the command instantly.

Impressed? You can see the brain works very hard, can't you? I think you can now see why the brain consumes the most food in the body. Even a robot using the latest computer technology is no match for the human brain. Our brain is superior to one, or even a slew of computers.

What is the dominant hand?

Do you throw a ball with your right or left hand? Do you know anyone who can throw a ball with either hand?

Do you write with your right or

left hand? Do you know anyone who can write or eat with either hand? The hand which you use most is called the "dominant hand."

Now let's confirm which is your dominant hand by using the "Edinburgh Handedness Inventory" and the handedness ratio formula.

Indicate your preferences in the use of hands in the following activities:

	right	left
1. Write quickly		
2. Draw figures and pictures		
3. Throw a ball		
4. Use scissors		
5. Use a tooth brush		
6. Use a knife		
7. Use a spoon		
8. Strike a match		
9. Grab the top of a broom		
10. Open a box		

①Choose right or left hand for each activity. Put a "ı" in the appropriate column.

②First, put + for the hand you usually use.

③Second, if you can use both hands, put + in both columns.

④If you use one hand exclusively, put another + in the appropriate box.

⑤Add up the+marks for each hand.

⑥Now calculate your handedness ratio:

Handedness Ratio = (Total points for right—total points for left) / Grand Total×100

Grand Total = Right + Left

If your handedness ratio is positive, you are right-handed. If it is negative, you are left-handed. The larger the ratio, the greater your handed inclination. Therefore a person who has plus 100% is exclusively right-handed, and a person who has minus 100% is exclusively left-handed. If your ratio is from minus 50% to plus 50%, you are able to use both hands equally. What about you? Ten percent of the world's population is said to be left-handed. The proportion of left-handed persons has never changed down the ages regardless of nationality, culture or race. No one knows the real reason for handedness or why the proportion of handedness is constant. It is a dark mystery. I thought that if I examined the relation between the dominant hand and the brain I could learn something interesting, so I decided to try an experiment.

Experiment:
Open and close your right and left palms

I am 100% right-handed. I investigated brain activity while I opened and closed the palms of both hands. When I opened and closed my dominant right palm, the area for commanding the movements of muscles on the left side of the cerebrum became active. If you are right-handed, with your left hand press your forehead on the left side and slightly back while moving your right hand. This is the area for commanding the right hand to move. In this way, the right side of the cerebrum is linked to the left hand, and the left side of the cerebrum is linked to the right hand. To put it another way: when you move one hand, the opposite side of the cerebrum becomes active. This fact is well known and often written about. However, the same is not true for your non-dominant hand. When I move my non-dominant left hand, not only the right side of the cerebrum, but the area for commanding the movements of muscles on the left side of the cerebrum is active. Until now no books have mentioned that when you move one hand, both sides of the cerebrum are active.

Here's what I think:

A right-handed person naturally uses the right hand a lot. Since the relationship between the hand and the cerebrum for commanding is reversed, the left side of the cerebrum is good at controlling exercises for a right-handed person. On the contrary the right side of the cerebrum is not so good at controlling exercises when the right-handed person is moving the left hand.

Fig.26 **Open and close your right palm.**

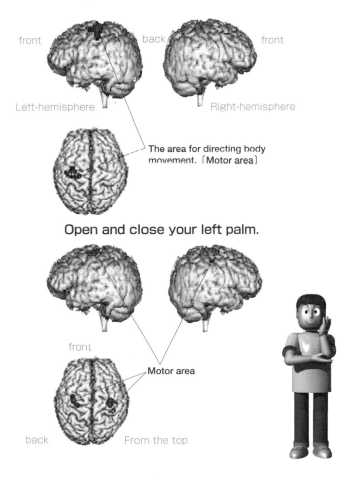

Open and close your left palm.

Motor area

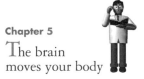

Chapter 5
The brain
moves your body

At that time the left side helps the right side.

I did the same experiment with a left-handed person and got an interesting result.

Whenever a left-handed person moves either the right or left only, both sides of the cerebrum are active. That means left-handers have a dual purpose cerebrum. Is a left-hander better at sports than a right-hander? I surveyed how many left-handed pitchers there are in professional baseball. I counted the number of left-handed pitchers on two professional teams who are left-handed hitters as well. Surprisingly enough, three in ten were left-handed. As I mentioned above, the average worldwide is one in ten.

Because both sides of the cerebrum control the movement, left-handed persons probably have an advantage in sports that use a ball, like tennis or baseball, which require skillful arm and hand movements.

Do skillful finger movements make the brain stronger?

Simple exercises like holding something with all five fingers, which we do routinely every day, are easy even for human babies and monkeys. However, more skillful movements of the fingers, like eating with a knife and fork, or buttoning a coat, which are also routine for us, cannot be done by babies or monkeys. Probably the brain functions very differently during simple and skillful movements of the fingers. Is the old saying "Skillful finger movements make the brain stronger" true?

I decided to investigate brain activity to differentiate simple from skillful movements of the fingers.

Experiment:
Simple and complex finger movements

A right-handed subject opening and closing his/her palm was chosen for the simple movement. For the complex movement, the subject rotated with his/her fingers two small balls with a diameter of about 3cm. According to the results of the experiment, the area for commanding muscle movement on the left side of the cerebrum was activated. When a right-handed person moved the dominant right hand, the reverse, left side of the cerebrum was activated. However, not one but both sides of the cerebrum were activated when the subject carried out complex movements. Various other areas were also active. Thus, complex finger move-

Fig.27

Simple finger movement.

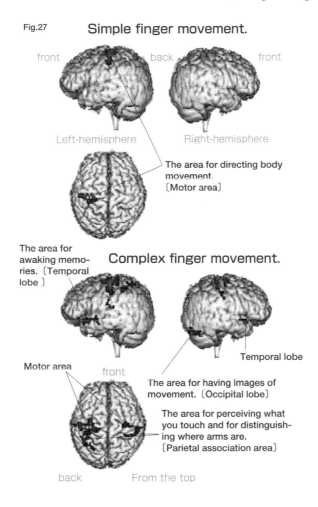

front   back   front

Left-hemisphere   Right-hemisphere

The area for directing body movement.
[Motor area]

The area for awaking memories. [Temporal lobe]

Complex finger movement.

Temporal lobe

Motor area   front

The area for having images of movement. [Occipital lobe]

The area for perceiving what you touch and for distinguishing where arms are.
[Parietal association area]

back   From the top

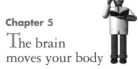

Chapter 5

The brain
moves your body

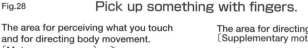

Fig.28 **Pick up something with fingers.**

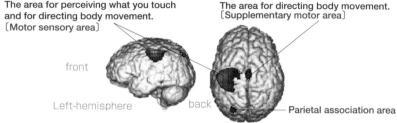

The area for perceiving what you touch and for directing body movement. [Motor sensory area]

The area for directing body movement. [Supplementary motor area]

front

Left-hemisphere   back

Parietal association area

Pick up something with a tool.

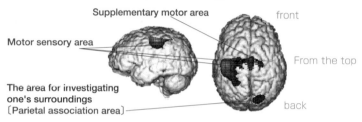

Supplementary motor area

Motor sensory area

front

From the top

The area for investigating one's surroundings [Parietal association area]

back

ments cause various areas of the cerebrum to become more active than simple movements.

Interestingly, the prefrontal cortex, which is believed to be linked to brain activity, is not active at these times.

Experiment: Pick up things with fingers or chopsticks

Fig 28 shows the brain activity of nine right-handed college students while they were using their right hands. When you pick something up, broader areas of the brain are active than when doing a simple exercise, like opening and closing the palm.

Furthermore if you use a tool like chopsticks, the active area will expand. Once again, the prefrontal cortex does not become active.

Regrettably, I cannot say for sure that complex finger exercises make the brain stronger. Only studying every day can do that. I can say that the cerebrum is more active during complex exercises, so maybe it's better to use chopsticks than a knife and fork.

When you are sleepy in class, or you cannot concentrate on an examination, try doing complex finger exercises. For example: rolling an eraser around in your palm, spinning a pencil around, or moving your fingers in other ways. I sometimes do these kinds of things if I get stuck while writing a paper or feel sleepy during a meeting. Strangely enough, such activities refresh me.

We've talked a lot about sports and the functions of the cerebrum. Have you been able to follow?

You have learned the marvelous fact that when you move your non-dominant hand, both sides of the cerebrum go to work.

You have also learned that it is not the case that complex finger exercises make the brain stronger. That's how discoveries in brain science can open the doors of the brain one after another.

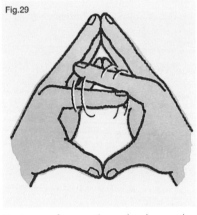

Fig.29

Moving your fingers with your hands crossed.

Chapter 5: Putting it all together

- Many parts of the brain are active while exercising, so the brain works very hard.
- The brain is more active when you do exercise with complex movements or use tools.
- Exercise alone does not activate the prefrontal cortex. It cannot be said that complex finger exercises make the brain stronger.

Chapter 5
The brain moves your body

Moving the body: The cerebellum and the basal ganglia

I have explained how the cerebrum works while moving the body in this chapter. The brain uses a sensing mechanism to constantly check to make sure the movements of the muscles are smooth. If the movements are not smooth, the brain instantly changes the command. Let me explain this mechanism in more detail. Please recall a time when you walked on a balance beam. You moved your arms and upper body constantly in order to maintain your balance. In the same way we humans are constantly balancing our bodies in daily life. The cerebellum and the basal ganglia work hard to perform this function. The basal ganglia is located deep inside the cerebrum. If this area were damaged, your limbs would tremble, you would not have voluntary muscle movement, and you would not be able to stop your muscles from moving. These problems would be caused by a shortage of dopamine, which is a neurotransmitter. This teaches us that the basal ganglia is active when you willingly control muscle movements. The cerebellum adjusts the command which the cerebrum issues to the muscles in order to have smooth muscle movements. Balancing the body and maintaining a proper posture is extremely important. In addition, the cerebellum is related to speedy and continuous movements, such as using both hands to play the piano.

Fig.30

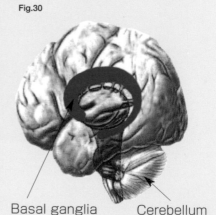

Basal ganglia   Cerebellum

Let's try 5

You can practice my experiments by following these instructions. Even without using
special equipment, your brain will work the
same as explained on pages 65 and 66.

Experiment:
Simple and complex finger movements

● How to do it:

1. Do a simple finger movement first. If
   you are right-handed open and close your
   right hand. If left-handed open and close
   your left hand.

2. For the complex movement, rotate two
   small balls with your dominant fingers.

3. If you don't have an appropriate size ball,
   rotate an eraser or a pencil with
   your fingers.

4. Pick up something small by using
   chop sticks or two pencils.

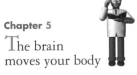

Chapter 5

The brain
moves your body

Your mind is in your brain

We have seen how the brain works during ordinary activities, like listening to people talking, studying, and moving your body. I believe you can understand the fact that all your activities are directed by the brain.

Do you think the brain controls what your heart feels as well? What about when you sense or feel emotions? What happens in your brain when you try to understand the feelings of others? Or when you are aware of yourself?

Do you think the brain causes feelings and emotions in the same way it does other human behaviors?

Long ago some people believed the mind was located in the heart because people died when the heart stopped beating. Others imagined that a soul existed apart from the body, and that was where the heart was.

I believe the mind is located in the brain, and the mind's activities are controlled by the brain. I have designed various kinds of experiments in order to confirm this. I would like to show you some of the evidence I have found.

By the way research in this field has only just begun. Mental activi-ties change depending on one's experiences and the environment in which one grew up. Therefore we can expect utterly different results the more we investigate. Please keep this in mind as you read further.

Where do likes and dislikes come from?

Do you have likes and dislikes? You probably have certain foods that you cannot even try to eat, and have favorite foods that you could eat every day. I love sushi and barbecued beef; I dislike vinegary foods and liver. Which part of the brain causes such likes and dislikes?

Experiment:
Answer whether you like or dislike something by looking at photographs of food

I investigated brain activity when two college student subjects stated their likes and dislikes while looking at photographs of food. Please compare the figures for "likes" and "dislikes."

Totally different parts of the brain are activated for "likes" and "dis-

Chapter 6

Your mind is in your brain

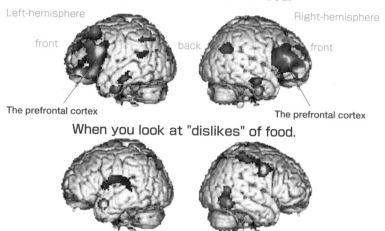

Fig.31

When you look at "likes" of food.

Left-hemisphere

front — back — front

Right-hemisphere

The prefrontal cortex

The prefrontal cortex

When you look at "dislikes" of food.

likes."

What are the main differences?

The prefrontal cortex for issuing the command to think is active while looking at foods that are liked. You think about such things as your mother's cooking or that you love sushi when you think about what you like, don't you? On the other hand, the prefrontal cortex is not active while looking at foods that are disliked. I think you answer the question automatically, because you simply dislike that particular food, and you don't have to think about it. I am afraid that's

because you never want to think about things you dislike.

Well what about affection for other people? First, I investigated the brain activity of four female college student subjects. They were shown various photographs of male students and asked if they felt they liked the person in the photo. Interestingly enough, when a subject answered "Yes," the area of the brain for detecting what you see was very active. When a subject answered "No," not that area, but the areas for learning the meaning of words and recalling memories were activated. Decisions about what you like are made in a flash. That is probably why first impressions are thought to be so important.

Next, I did the same experiment with six male students. The areas of the brain related to instinct were activated when the subjects answered "Yes."

Instinct can be explained by brain activities that issue commands to eat and sleep for survival, and produce feelings of pleasure, sorrow and anger. Meanwhile when a subject answered "No," the prefrontal cortex for thinking was activated. In this way, when a subject answered "No," different areas of the brain were activated depending on the subject's gender. When you say "I like this person" you use the area of the brain for detecting what you see if you are female, and you use your instinct if you are male. However, when you say "I don't like this person" the area related to words is active in females, and the prefrontal cortex is active in males. We are all humans but men and women think differently. Don't you think that's interesting?

Reading a person's face

People use two ways to communicate ideas and feelings. The first is verbal communication. I showed you what happens in the brain when you try to understand conversation on page21.

The second is communication by expression and tone of voice. I believe you can read your parents' and friends' faces easily when they feel pleasure, sorrow or anger. Also you can understand a person's feelings from their tone of voice, such as shouting, or a silky voice. Here is what I found out when I investigated brain activity during these kinds of communication.

Experiment:
Try to understand the feelings of others by looking at photographs showing various expressions

All the subjects were right-handed so the area for producing words was on the left side of the prefrontal cortex. The area on the right side of the prefrontal cortex was activated, the opposite side for producing

Chapter 6

Your mind is in your brain

words. The results appear in Fig.32. I also did an experiment with right-handed subjects trying to understand the feelings of others by the tone of their voices and got the same results.

Now we clearly know that right-handed people use the left side of the prefrontal cortex for verbal communication, and the right side for nonverbal communication. I am afraid that a right-handed person who cannot understand others' feelings at all is not good at using the right side of the brain.

Who am I ?

I firmly believe that I am me, and that I am different from other peo-ple; furthermore, other people will never understand everything there is to know about me. Do you feel the same way?

Now I would like to ask you, "Who are you?" Have you ever thought about this question? Something happened to me in high school that started me thinking about the question of who I was.

What happened?

In many ways I was precocious for my age, and I already liked a certain girl when I was in first grade. When I changed schools in third grade I liked another girl ... and then a third girl in junior high school. Whenever I sat next to her I was in rapture, but alas, my affections were not returned. I was

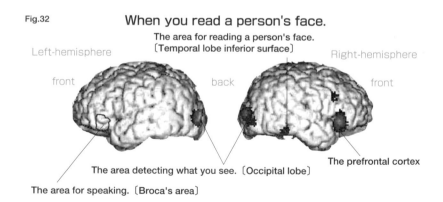

Fig.32

When you read a person's face.

The area for reading a person's face.
〔Temporal lobe inferior surface〕

Left-hemisphere

Right-hemisphere

front   back   front

The area detecting what you see. 〔Occipital lobe〕

The prefrontal cortex

The area for speaking. 〔Broca's area〕

shocked by this rejection. When I was alone I found myself wondering, "What is she doing now?" At these times it felt like she was right there with me. I wondered, "Am I imagining all this? Is she really here with me? What is human existence? Do I exist?" I knew human beings must die someday and that my existence must end, too. I even thought about how to stop from dying because I hated to accept the fact of human death. And then a thought suddenly occurred to me:

"Every human being has his or her own experience; what is seen, what is heard, what is studied, what has to be done, and so on. Memories are produced by our experiences, and of course every person is unique. My memories distinguish me from others.

"If so, if I could store my unique memories in a computer, I could survive forever, even without my body, as long as the computer's batteries stayed charged. Since memories are in the brain, all I need to do is create a way to transfer my memories to the computer."

And that is how I came to be interested in the brain by the time I entered high school.

A broken heart led me to brain science.

But now I have to ask again, "Who am I ?"

Where are memories located?

Since becoming a brain scientist I have thought a great deal about how the mind, that is the brain, comes to be aware of who we are. Although it is an impossible dream, what would happen if I could actually transplant my brain into your body? Although your body is yours, after the transplant operation, if asked, you would answer "My name is Ryuta Kawashima." You would go to the laboratory and study brain science in your child body. You wouldn't go to your home after work, but go to Ryuta Kawashima's home. And you would drink beer, watch TV and tell children your age to study. On weekends you would play video games with other kids. All these things would happen if my brain were in your body.

Well, what happens in your head when you are aware of yourself? As a matter of fact, this is one of the great unsolved mysteries in brain

Chapter 6

Your mind is in your brain

science. It may take some time to find the answer. Memories are considered one of the key factors in solving the mystery. The idea that suddenly occurred to me when I was a high-school student was not wrong. However, just storing my memories in a computer would create a computer storeroom, not a human brain. The brain is a complex mechanism, but it is obvious that memories are an essential part of that mechanism. So, I investigated brain activity involved in memorizing.

Experiment:
Look at photographs and answer whether you recognize the person or scene

Fig.33   **When you look at photographs of a face.**

The area for judging whether something is familiar or not.
[Anterior temporal cortex]

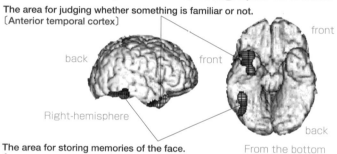

back   front   front

Right-hemisphere

back

The area for storing memories of the face.
[Inferior temporal cortex]   From the bottom

When you look at photographs of a scene.

Anterior temporal cortex

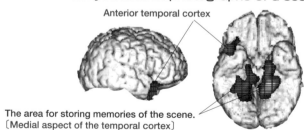

The area for storing memories of the scene.
[Medial aspect of the temporal cortex]

First, there is an area that is activated by either a photograph of a face or scene. This area is probably for judging whether something is familiar or not. Both the memories of a face or scene are stored in a drawer located slightly off to the side and underneath the cerebrum. This is the area for detecting what you see.

In another experiment I investigated brain activity when a person tried to remember the names of animals, plants, a TV, a radio and other common items by looking at photographs. Look at Fig.34. Different areas are used for storing the names of different things. The

Fig.34 **When you try to remember the names of animals.**

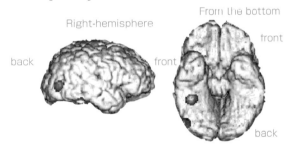

When you try to remember the names of plants.

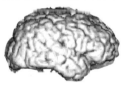

When you try to remember the names of artifacts

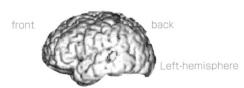

Chapter 6

Your mind is in your brain

area for storing animal names is the same area which is activated when you see. In this way memories are stored in various locations in the brain. Many researchers have confirmed the fact that the prefrontal cortex, which does the highest-level work in the brain, is activated when retrieving memories from these places.

Where is the memory of one's own face stored? In a drawer deep within the left side of the cerebrum in the area related to instinct.

As I explained in the section on likes and dislikes, this is the area that issues commands to eat and sleep for survival, and produces feelings of pleasure, sorrow and anger.

Therefore, memories of oneself are different from other memories, are needed for survival, and have a strong relation to feelings. For example, you can clearly remember an incident that was especially happy or painful, can't you? When I was in second grade, I hit a car with a stone that I hit with a bat; after which I was severely scolded. Another time I dropped my lunch just as I was about to eat with my friend in the park. I had been look-ing forward to having lunch with my friend so I was of course miserable. These embarrassing memories are still alive in me. The memories themselves are insignificant, but they were a great shock to me at the time so I can still remember them vividly.

Research into the relationship between the mind and the brain started slowly but it is progressing rapidly. With the invention of more advanced equipment we will be able to see where our mind is located. Will it be in the brain or outside of the body?

Perhaps we will someday be able to prove the existence of the soul scientifically.

Chapter 6: Putting it all together

- Research into the relationship between the mind and the brain has begun.
- Although the activities of the mind are thought to be directed by the brain, there are still many more experiments that need to be done before even a few of the mysteries are solved.

Chapter 6

Your mind is
in your brain

Understanding more about the brain —6
The area deep in the cerebrum

The memory of one's own face is stored in an area deep within the left side of the cerebrum. This area is part of the "cerebrum limbic system." The cerebrum limbic system is located in the paleocortex. What is the paleocortex? Have you ever heard of the theory of evolution? According to this theory, human beings evolved from apes. Living things evolved over the ages into millions of species. Mammals such as apes evolved from reptiles like snakes and amphibians like frogs. Although many argue about evolution, the simple fact is this: Reptiles and amphibians indeed have a cerebrum which works in the same way as our paleocortex. This indicates that reptiles and amphibians may very well be our ancestors. The prefix "paleo-" means old. We use "paleo" for the cortex, because the functions of the paleocortex are essential for survival: eating, sleeping, reproduction and the "fight or flight" instinct. This is of course how the brains of animals help them to survive in the natural world. Aren't you surprised to learn we have the same brain as frogs and snakes?

Now what is the neocortex? It begins with the prefix "neo," which is the opposite of "paleo." It's the surface of the cerebrum which works the same way as a mammal's cerebrum. Mammals are our closest ancestors. As a matter of fact almost all the human activities which I explained in this book—reading books, listening to conversations and music, calculating, studying and moving the body—are the work of the neocortex. The behaviors that make us uniquely human are the handiwork of the neocortex.

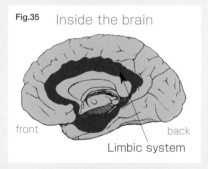

Fig.35 Inside the brain

front   back

Limbic system

Let's try 6

You can practice my experiments by following these instructions. Even without using special equipment, your brain will work the same as explained on pages 76.

Experiment:
Look at photographs and answer whether you recognize the person or scene.

● How to do it:

1. This experiment requires two or more persons.
2. Each member brings photographs of someone's face or a scene.
3. Mix up the photographs and stack them up.
4. Look at a photograph and if you find it familiar, say "Yes."
5. After one person finishes, shuffle the photos and repeat.

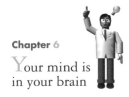

Chapter 6

Your mind is
in your brain

Conclusion: Train your brain your self

Have you ever thought "I think like an adult; I almost look like an adult, so why do you treat me like a kid?"

What is the difference in size between an adult's and a child's brain? In Fig. 36 is my brain, and that of a 7th grader (12 years old) and a first grader.

This is a cross section image of the part of the brain located in the forehead. Having read this far, I am sure you wouldn't be surprised no matter how we sliced and diced the images of the brain! What differences do you notice? Size and shape of course, but anything else?

Your brain is developing right now

Let's take a closer look at the patterns of the cross-sectional images. You can see a gray band inside of the inner surface of the brain. You can also see a whitish area. The gray band is full of brain cells, which I compared to the many tiny pieces of a mosaic picture on page45. We have several hundred billion cells in our brains. The number of cells remains almost the same from birth. The volume of gray matter is just about the same in all three subjects.

Fig.36

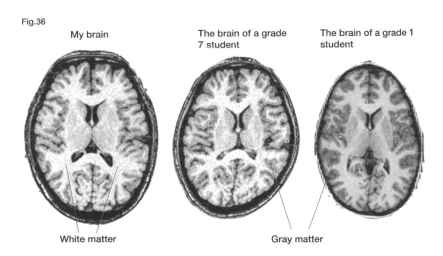

My brain

The brain of a grade 7 student

The brain of a grade 1 student

White matter

Gray matter

Chapter 7

Conclusion: Train your brain your self

Now take a look at the whitish area. In this area brain cells extend ten, even twenty "hands" and they are linked together. In this book we call these hands roads or paths.

Comparing the whitish areas among the three, mine is the largest. This means a child's brain has fewer linkages among the brain cells than an adult's brain.

A newborn baby's brain weighs only 400g. At four or five years old it's 1200g, or three times that of a newborn. An adult's brain is 1300~1400g. As I mentioned before, the number of brain cells stays the same, so the increased weight is the result of adding more and more hands. The prefrontal cortex is particularly busy developing brain cell linkages up until you are 20 years old.

Your brain is in the midst of this development. The more varied your studies and experiences, the more your brain will develop. Your brain development will match your efforts 100%.

Since I was once your age, I know how much you like to play. But please remember: Your brain is developing the most right now. Studying throughout your school-days, from primary to high school, is the most important thing you can do for the development of your brain.

Keep the prefrontal cortex active

I have tried as much as possible not to use scientific terms, as you are new to brain science.

However I used one term, the prefrontal cortex, because it is far larger and better developed in humans than in any other animal, and functions as the commander, directing other areas of the brain. The human prefrontal cortex has grown larger along with the process of evolution. As I said before, the prefrontal cortex grows with the accumulation of brain cell linkages. Let me put it another way: It takes twenty years for the prefrontal cortex of a grown-up to complete making its network of brain cells. The large prefrontal cortex distinguishes us from other animals.

Here's a question for you: What do you think would happen if you did not activate the brain cells of the prefrontal cortex sufficiently, and your brain could not develop a proper network of brain cells? Think about it ...

I have explained how to activate brain cells in order to develop your prefrontal cortex. When you think, read, calculate and study, the brain cells of the prefrontal cortex become very active. Just hearing and seeing without actively thinking does nothing for the prefrontal cortex. Of course just believing what people say is not enough. You need to investigate, think and decide for yourself.

Throughout your life, your parents, teachers and other grown-ups around you have helped you to develop your brain. You are now entering the phase in your life where you can develop your brain yourself. You cannot develop a strong brain as long as you always take the easy way out, and just do what you like and not do what bores you. You must take the lead. You must develop your brain yourself.

A mountain of pearls

Imagine we had a time machine and you could go back a thousand years and tell people what you had learned in school and read in books. What would happen? People would think you were a genius. What about a hundred years ago? The same.

Why would they think that? Because you would know all the things that had been discovered and invented for a hundred or a thousand years. Everything you have learned in school and read in a book is like a pearl gathered over time and kept for you by our ancestors. These are the pearls of human wisdom and knowledge. Studying is the only way to collect these pearls for yourself. Don't study just for good marks, but to become wealthy in wisdom and knowledge.

In conclusion, I would like to convey the most important idea:

The universe has existed from time immemorial. The earth was born 4.6 billion years ago. The first creature appeared 4 billion years ago, and life has evolved into various kinds of plants and animals. Our ancestors descended from hominids five million years ago, and we have been evolving ever since. We human beings stand at the front of a long line of time flowing down the ages. The most

Chapter 7

Conclusion:
Train your brain
your self

important role you have is to pass on the wisdom of the ages to the next generation. Better yet, discover something no one else has thought about, apply the tools in your brain to it, and add a few new pearls to the mountain of wisdom and knowledge.

If reading this book has sparked in you an interest in brain science, please visit my laboratory after you become a college student. Let's explore the world of the brain together.

I have explained various brain functions in this book, but what we don't know about the brain would fill hundreds or even thousands of books. We have only a handful of knowledge. Many researchers at universities and institutions around the world are working hard to advance brain science, but in order to solve all the mysteries of the brain we still need your help. Please add your pearls to ours. We are waiting for you to join us.

There is nothing I would like more than to climb that mountain of pearls with you, solving all the mysteries of the brain along the way!

Understanding more about the brain —7
The total structure of the brain

I would like to give you a simple explanation of the parts of the brain and their functions. I will skip the cerebrum since I have talked a lot about it already. The cerebellum is located under the cerebrum. The cerebellum is closely related to the control of muscle movements, including strength and power. It is also related to learning how to move. If the cerebellum doesn't work properly, movements will be stiff like a robot's. "Mesencephalon," "pons," "medulla oblongata" are located from top to bottom in front of the cerebellum. There is "spinal cord" underneath the medulla oblongata. The mesencephalon controls senses and movements. The pons communicates information about movements from the cerebrum to the cerebellum. The medulla oblongata has an important role relating to survival: controlling digestion, breathing and the heart. The spinal cord's function is related to controlling the body's exercises and also detecting sensation from the skin, muscles and joints. Although you cannot see it because its boundary is not clear, the diencephalon is on top of the mesencephalon. It consists of two parts: the thalamus, which communicates sense information to the cerebrum, and the hypothalamus, which maintains body temperature and adjusts the functions of the internal organs and blood vessels. The diencephalon, mesencephalon, pons and medulla oblongata are collectively called the brain stem.

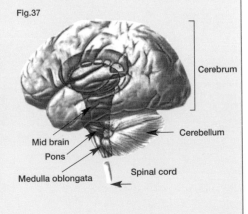

Fig.37

Cerebrum

Cerebellum

Mid brain

Pons

Spinal cord

Medulla oblongata

Chapter 7

Conclusion:
Train your brain
your self

Functional localization of the brain

I have explained that our brain does not work as a chunk but as a combination of different functions. This is called in brain science the "functional localization of the brain." A Canadian brain surgeon, Dr. Wilder Penfield, discovered "functional localization of the brain" more than fifty years ago. Dr. Penfield tried to electrically stimulate various spots on the surface of the brain during surgery. When he did so he found something interesting. When he stimulated a certain point on the surface of the brain, the subject's hand moved automatically. When he tried another point, the subject's leg moved. He also found that the subject felt as if his hand were being touched if a certain spot on the surface of the brain was stimulated. He also developed a map of the brain, often portrayed as a cartoon called the motor homunculus. The map shows us what part of the body moves when a spot is stimulated. By the way, don't worry about pain when the brain is electrically stimulated. Our brain cannot sense pain. So what's a headache? Actually the pain does not come from the brain; it comes from the nerves on the surface of the head.

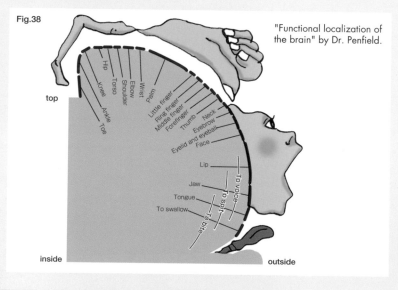

Fig.38

"Functional localization of the brain" by Dr. Penfield.

top

Hip
Knee
Torso
Ankle
Shoulder
Toe
Elbow
Wrist
Palm
Little finger
Ring finger
Middle finger
Forefinger
Thumb
Neck
Eyebrow
Eyelid and eyeball
Face
Lip
To voice
Jaw
To spit
Tongue
To swallow
To bite

inside

outside

Understanding more about the brain —9
Brain death

I think you have heard of "brain death." It's gained a lot of attention lately because of its relation to organ transplants. I am afraid it's a bit difficult to understand, but it's an important issue. Please consider it. First, what is brain death? This means the whole brain, including the brain stem for survival, has completely stopped working and will never return to its former state. Once someone is brain dead, the heart and breathing stop immediately and that person dies. What is referred to as a "vegetative state" means that only the cerebrum has stopped working, but the heart and lungs are still working because the brain stem is still functioning. This is different from brain death.

Human death was once defined as when the heart and breathing stopped, and the pupils of the eyes become dilated and fixed. However the definition has changed. Even if your heart and breathing stop, modern medicine can keep you alive using a heart-lung machine. Even if a doctor says that a patient's brain has stopped working, it is difficult to accept that the patient is dead, because that person is still warm to the touch. Have there been any cases where brain death was misdiagnosed? Is it possible for the brain to suddenly start working again?

Why has the idea that brain death equals human's death become so important? It is because of organ transplants. There are many people with serious diseases of the heart, lungs, liver and kidneys who only have one chance to survive: To get a healthy organ from another person. Since the fresher the organ is, the better the result, doctors are keen to remove an organ from a brain-dead patient and transplant it as quickly as possible. This medical treatment has become quite common, and has saved countless lives. Even the bereaved family can feel some small joy knowing that their loved one has saved another person's life. Someday in the future when an artificial organ is invented that can function just like a human organ, we will have no need for organ transplants. I believe thinking about death is just as important as thinking about life. The next time you read or hear about organ transplants in the newspaper or on TV talk with your family about it.

Understanding more about the brain —10
Is it possible to transplant a brain?

A lung transplant was performed recently at Tohoku University where I work. Have you ever thought of the possibility of transplanting a brain from a donor who has a serious disease to the body of a person who is brain dead? As a matter of fact I used to think about the possibility when I was young. Is there a possibility? The answer is no, not now at least, but it may be possible in the near future. However I am positive no doctor would actually do it. Do you know why I am so sure?

Let's say John had a lung transplant. Afterward he would still be John, but with a donor's lung. But if John got a brain transplant from, say, Alice, who would John be? John or Alice? While you are thinking about that, take a look at page 75 in Chapter 6.

Understanding more about the brain —11
The brain gets old, too.

Just like the rest of the body, the brain gets old and eventually dies. This process of life applies to you and me, and all humans. No one knows why our body and brain get old or why we cannot survive forever. There may be many reasons, but we don't have all the answers yet.

The brains of old people are shriveled with wide wrinkles like those on the hands and feet. Actually I learned from images of my own brain that it was a bit shriveled compared to those of young college students. No matter how well you take care of yourself, your brain will get old just like your body. According to the results of a study I did with my colleagues, more aged men than women had shriveled brains. We found the frontal lobe and the parietal lobe are the most susceptible to aging. Furthermore we found this phenomenon in areas filled with nuclei but not with axons. This tells us that axons may not deteriorate along with aging.

We have learned in this book that the work of the brain means the work of the nuclei, which are in the network connected by axons.

Therefore if you continue to expand the brain network, the brain's performance will not decline along with aging.

Well how can you keep up the brain network? Unfortunately no one has the answer. From my research I thought that stimulating the brain was important, but tapping your head is not going to stimulate it. So what does?

Don't you sometimes feel that time is standing still? You want to advance in school, be a grown-up soon, but unfortunately time doesn't fly.

On the other hand, maybe you have heard your parents say that time goes by too fast? I once felt like you that the days were too long, but after graduating from college, I gradually began to feel the days were too short.

When you are young, you can learn a lot and experience a lot and your brain is always being stimulated. On the other hand as you get older, you learn and experience fewer new things and your brain becomes less stimulated.

Recently I investigated brain activity in old people who went sightseeing for a week in Okinawa, a famous tourist spot in Japan. It turned out that their brains were more active after the trip than before. To stimulate the brain, try learning something new, like traveling to a new place, or experiencing something you never tried before. Why not try studying with your grandpa and grandma. You can teach them the secret of how to stop the brain from aging.

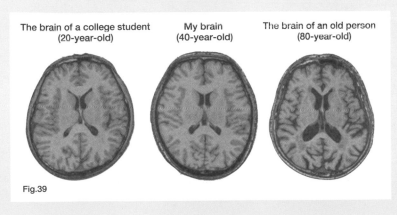

The brain of a college student (20-year-old)　My brain (40-year-old)　The brain of an old person (80-year-old)

Fig.39

Dear Readers,

How was it? I have concentrated on explaining the workings of the brain based on brain imaging research. Was it difficult for you? At a minimum I hope you will take away from reading this book the following three points:

1. The brain is a vast mystery, and it is vastly interesting to study brain science
2. Since your brain is developing day by day, it is very important to study every day.
3. You can train your brain yourself.

Your brain has unlimited potential to do anything. For the brightest future possible, train your brain yourself. Do it by learning a lot, reading books, doing sports and playing with your friends. As a grown-up I envy you and your brilliant potential.

Dear Parents and Grown-ups,

Currently the three mainstays of brain science are: creating the brain, protecting the brain and knowing the brain. Brain imaging research, which I have been studying at Tohoku University, is in the latter group of the studies. In scientific circles what I do is known as non-invasive functional brain imaging. We call it "mapping" because we locate the exact place of individual functions in the brain as accurately and in as much detail as possible. It has not been long since the research started in the early 1980s, making it one of the latest frontiers of research in Japan.

Two and a half years have already passed since I published the original "Train Your Brain" in Japanese. The book presented the latest research at the time, and its message was: It seems easy, but reading and calculating are the best ways to train your brain. As a matter of fact, I was surprised to find that such easy tasks activated so many parts of the brain, especially the prefrontal cortex. Until very recently brain science had mistakenly maintained that calculation was directed by part of the parietal lobe and reading was directed by parts of the parietal and temporal lobes.

However the progress of brain science has been rapid, and so I would like to introduce some of what has been discovered since the Japanese edition of this book came out.

This image shows us the faster you read in your native language, the more active your brain is. Despite the fact that your prefrontal cortex does not work when reading fast silently, it does work hard when reading fast aloud. That is to say it is important to read fast when you read aloud. Likewise I investigated brain activity while calculating at different speeds. As you can see in the image, the faster you solve calculations, the more active the brain is, including the prefrontal cortex. Thus, not only reading aloud and doing simple calculation, but doing them quickly is very important. Other activities which activate the prefrontal cortex besides reading aloud and doing simple calculation have also been found recently.

The image shows us the activity of the prefrontal cortex while a sixth grade student is telling his mother what happened at school that day. We used something called optical topography for this experiment. As you can see the red area, the pre-

Read a native language loudly and quickly

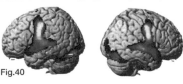

Fig.40

Read a native language silently and quickly

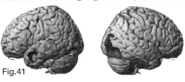

Fig.41

Solve single digit additions quickly

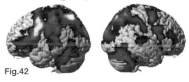

Fig.42

Solve single digit additions slowly

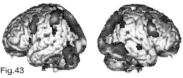

Fig.43

Fig.44
The brain activity while talking with your mother.

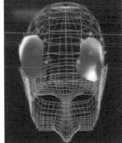

frontal cortex of both sides is very active. Now you can see how very important communication between parents and children is to developing a child's brain.

In July 2003 I published my new book, *"Develop your Brain"* for Japanese children. I hope you will read it in English soon.

Ryuta Kawashima
July 2003

Postscript for the English edition

Two and a half years have passed since my first book "Train your Brain" was published in Japanese. I am glad to hear that many children, families, and school teachers all over Japan have read, and hopefully profited, from my book.

I would like to express my sincere gratitude to Mr. R. Fujito for translating my book into English. With the publication of this English edition, I hope as many children as possible all over the world will be able to reach their full unlimited potential by learning how to study and train their brain.

Ryuta Kawashima
Autumn 2003

Acknowledgements

Brain study cannot be pursued alone. Were it not for the support of many and the understanding of my family, I would be unable to carry on my studies. I would like to thank my colleagues and friends: Prof. Taira at Nihon University Medical School and Dr. Nakamura at the Kyoto University Primate Research Institute for their great cooperation, Mr. Sugiura at Tohoku University Graduate School for the supreme efforts he put into all the experiments, and Ms. Sato and Ms. Watanabe who did all the complicated office work.

Concerning the publishing of this book, I would like to thank Mr. Tani for his advice and cooperation without which this book would never have seen the light of day. I also wish to express my appreciation to the editor in chief, Mr. Hara, and Mr. Okita at the Kumon Research Center for giving me the opportunity to write this book.

We used positron CT equipment thanks to the collaboration of the Ministry of Health, the Longevity Science Research Center and Japan Radioisotope Association Nishina Memorial Foundation, and the functional MRI equipment thanks to Nihon University Medical School and Tohoku Fukushi University Kansei Fukushi Research Center. I wish to thank all those who cooperated with me on my investigation at these facilities.

My research has been subsidized by the Ministry of Education, Culture, Sports, Science and Technology, and the Japan Society for the Promotion of Science.

About the Author

RYUTA KAWASHIMA, Ph.D., is a professor at Tohoku University. He trained in medicine at Tohoku University and gained a Ph.D. there. Previously he studied at Karolinska Institute in Sweden. He is the latest frontier of Brain Imaging in Japan. He was born in Chiba, Japan, in 1959.

Translator

RYOKEN FUJITO
In addition to being a translator, he is also ERF's spokesperson. He established a translation company, ERF LLP (http://er-f.com) to give himself an outlet to leverage his international business experience gained while working overseas. Born in Japan, 1954.